1961

Nicholas D. Kazarinoff

The University of Michigan

Analytic
Inequalities

HOLT, RINEHART AND WINSTON
New York

Preface

In 1934, Hardy, Littlewood, and Pólya completed their pioneering and unique work *Inequalities* (Cambridge University Press). Since that time, brief treatments of the topics of their Chapter II have been published in other languages, notably Russian, but no short monograph on the elementary portions of the subject has appeared in English. This is the more distressing since *Inequalities* demands so much mathematical sophistication of its readers as to be unsuitable for nearly all our undergraduate mathematics students. Mathematicians know that mathematical analysis is largely a systematic study and exploitation of inequalities, but students are unaccustomed to mathematics involving anything but inequalities. I have long felt that if freshmen and sophomores were on friendly terms with inequalities, especially elementary geometric ones, then they would find the "epsilon and delta" language which is basic to the calculus less mysterious. In fact, I believe that the majority of calculus students are capable of understanding their subject provided they have had previous training in the significance and use of inequalities.

A revolution is taking place in mathematical curriculums, and all at once a number of elementary tracts on inequalities are to appear. At the high-school level, the School Mathematics Study Group Monograph Project is bringing out two monographs on elementary inequalities, one dealing primarily with geometric inequalities. If they become widely read, students will be much better prepared to cope with the concepts of continuity, derivative, and integral. However, even in our superior college texts, the role played by inequalities outside of the study of limits is a minor one. Theorems of real depth are thereby ignored. The major concept of *approximation* is perforce neglected. For example, if one has an exact formula, its use may entail considerable investigation involving inequalities. When a number—such as $\sin 2.35$, $(2 + \sqrt{3})^{\sqrt{5}}$, or $\int_0^1 e^{-x^2}\,dx$— which appears in some formula is replaced by a rational number, it is often vital to know the error introduced. Error estimates are expressed in terms of inequalities. Mathematical analysis itself is devoted to finding judicious approximations for integrals, infinite sums, solutions of differential equations, etc., without which conclusions could not be reached and

▼

theorems proved. These approximations are expressed in terms of inequalities.

In writing this pamphlet, I have attempted to achieve three objectives: to fill—at least partly—the gaps referred to above, to discuss inequalities which are basic tools in the development of modern mathematical theories, and to give a glimpse of the spirit and lifeblood of mathematical analysis. The topics treated are sufficiently introduced by the Table of Contents. The deepest and most difficult—Bernstein's proof of the Weierstrass Approximation Theorem and the Cauchy, Bunyakovskiĭ, Hölder, and Minkowski Inequalities—I have left to the last. However, I warn the reader that problems within groups have not always been ordered in degree of difficulty. Many of them are rather hard. Not knowing which, he may solve them more easily. I believe that the reader will not find many places where I have been wordy, and I caution him to work with pencil and paper at hand for amplifying arguments and for supplying omitted details and computations. Moreover, there are never too many figures in a mathematics book, and although I have furnished illustrations in key spots, there will be several where the reader can beneficially construct his own.

The sustainer of my writing has been my wife, and it is she who typed the manuscript from my scrawled holograph while children shouted in her ears and tugged at her skirts. Her reward shall be whatever enjoyment the following pages bring.

N.D.K.

Ann Arbor, Michigan
June, 1960

Contents

[1]

Fundamentals

1. The Algebra of Inequalities

The inequalities we shall discuss will, for the most part, be statements about real numbers—positive, negative, and zero. The precise definition of a real number is subtle and nonelementary. A lucid discussion of it and related notions is to be found in *A Course of Pure Mathematics* by G. H. Hardy (Cambridge Univ. Press, 1938) or *Mathematical Analysis* by T. M. Apostol (Addison-Wesley Pub. Co., 1957). A good intuitive idea of what real numbers are and acquaintance with their basic properties is sufficient background for what is to follow here. Whenever use is made of a fundamental, but at the same time subtle, property of the real number system, attention will be called to the fact, and the property will be specifically described. On several occasions we shall use complex numbers. A reader who is unfamiliar with the complex numbers and their arithmetic can either ignore the material involving them; or, if he should be interested, he can obtain whatever prerequisites he needs by consulting *Analytic Function Theory*, Vol. 1, by Einar Hille (Ginn & Co., 1959).

By far the most important property of the real number system which we shall use is that the real numbers are ordered. This fact is recognized in our everyday association of the real numbers with points on a straight line. Our experience with measuring sticks dates from childhood, and as we have grown, we have associated larger and larger classes of numbers with larger and larger classes of points on a line until we have finally considered each point on a straight line to be associated with a unique real number. A line for which this association has been made is often referred to as the *real line*. An image of the real line is illustrated in Figure 1.

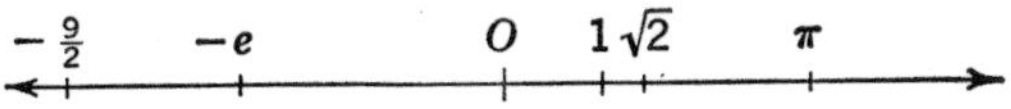

FIGURE 1

It can be proved on the basis of the definition of the real number system that it does indeed possess the natural order which we assign to it. However, we shall consider the property of order to be self-evident. It is explicitly described by the following postulates.

Postulate 1. The real number system contains a subset P the elements of which are called positive reals and which has the following properties.

Postulate 2. If a is a real number, then precisely one of the following three alternatives is true: a is in P, $-a$ is in P, a is 0.

Postulate 3. If a and b are in P, then $a + b$ and $a \cdot b$ are in P.

If a is in P, we write $a > 0$. If a is not in P and a is not zero, we say a is negative. The importance of the above postulates will become obvious in the paragraphs below.

Definition 1. $a > b$ (or equivalently, $b < a$) if and only if $a - b > 0$; that is, $a > b$ if and only if there is a positive number h such that $a = b + h$.

The statement "$a > b$" is, of course, read as "a is greater than b." Such a statement is called an inequality. Geometrically, the assertion $a > b$ means that the point representing the number a on the image of the real line illustrated above is to the right of the point representing b.

Incidentally, it is easy to show by Postulates 2 and 3 that the real numbers $1, 2, 3, \cdots$ are all in P. For suppose that 1 is not in P. Then since $1 \neq 0$, -1 is in P by Postulate 2. Therefore, by Postulate 3, $(-1)(-1)$ is in P. But $(-1)(-1) = 1$, which is not in P. This is a contradiction. Consequently, by Postulate 2, 1 is in P. Postulate 3 now guarantees that $2, 3, 4, \cdots$ are all in P. [NOTE: This proof is not as good as it might seem since one really needs to *prove* that $(-1)(-1) = 1$.]

EXERCISES

1. Similarly show that if $a < b < 0$, then $ab > 0$.
2. Similarly show that if $a < 0 < b$, then $ab < 0$.

The following fundamental rules of algebra for inequalities are proved using the postulates of order given above. Here and henceforward, lower case italic letters $a, b, c, \cdots$ will stand for real numbers unless otherwise stated.

Theorem 1. (*Determinativeness*). Given two real numbers a and b, exactly one of the following alternatives holds: $a > b$, $a = b$, $a < b$.

Proof. By Postulate 2, exactly one of the alternatives $a - b > 0$, $-(a - b) > 0$, $a - b = 0$ holds. By Definition 1, if $a - b > 0$, then $a > b$; if $-(a - b) > 0$, then $b > a$; and if $a - b = 0$, then $a = b$.∎

The symbol ∎ will always be used as an abbreviation of the sentence: This completes the proof. If either one of the alternatives $a < b$ or $a = b$ holds, then we write $a \leq b$—read as "a is less than or equal to b." For example, $2 \leq 2$ and $1 \leq 2$.

Theorem 2. (*Transitivity*). If $a > b$ and $b > c$, then $a > c$.

Proof. By Definition 1 and the hypothesis of the theorem, there exist positive numbers h and k such that $a = b + h$ and $b = c + k$. Therefore, $a = c + (h + k)$. Now, by Postulate 3, $h + k$ is positive; hence, $a > c$ by Definition 1.

Theorem 3. If $a > b$ and $c > d$, then $a + c > b + d$.

Proof. By hypothesis and Definition 1, there exist positive numbers h and k such that $a = b + h$ and $c = d + k$. Therefore, $a + c = b + d + (h + k)$; and hence by Postulate 3 and Definition 1, $a + c > b + d$. ∎

Theorem 4. If $a > b$ and $c > 0$, then $ac > bc$ and $\dfrac{a}{c} > \dfrac{b}{c}$. If $c < 0$, then $ac < bc$ and $\dfrac{a}{c} < \dfrac{b}{c}$.

Proof. This is an exercise for the reader.

Corollary. If $a > b > 0$, then $\dfrac{1}{a} < \dfrac{1}{b}$; if $a > 0 > b$, then $\dfrac{1}{a} > \dfrac{1}{b}$; if $a < b < 0$, then $\dfrac{1}{b} < \dfrac{1}{a}$.

Proof. Suppose $a > b > 0$ and $\dfrac{1}{a} \geq \dfrac{1}{b}$. Then by Theorem 4 with $c = ab$, which is positive by Postulate 3,

$$ab \cdot \frac{1}{a} \geq ab \cdot \frac{1}{b} \quad \text{or} \quad b \geq a.$$

By Postulate 2, this contradicts the hypothesis that $a > b$.

Next suppose $a > 0 > b$. Now, $a \cdot b < 0$. If this were not so, both ab and $a(-b)$, which is equal to $-ab$, would be in P. Postulate 2 guarantees that this is not the case. Thus, by Theorem 4, if we suppose that $\dfrac{1}{a} \leq \dfrac{1}{b}$, we conclude that

$$ab \cdot \frac{1}{a} \geq ab \cdot \frac{1}{b} \quad \text{or} \quad a \leq b.$$

This contradicts the hypothesis; hence, by Postulate 2,

$$\frac{1}{a} > \frac{1}{b}.$$

The proof of the last assertion in the Corollary is similar. ∎

Theorem 5.   If $a > b > 0$ and $c > d > 0$, then $ac > bd$ and $\dfrac{a}{d} > \dfrac{b}{c}$.

Proof.   As in previous arguments, there exist positive numbers h and k such that $a = b + h$ and $c = d + k$.   Therefore,

$$ac = bd + h(d + k) + k(b + h);$$

hence by Definition 1 and Postulate 3,

$$ac > bd.$$

To prove that $\dfrac{a}{d} > \dfrac{b}{c}$, we multiply both members of the inequality $ac > bd$ by $(cd)^{-1}$ and use Theorem 4. ∎

Theorem 6.   If $a > b > 0$ and p and q are positive integers, then

$$a^{p/q} > b^{p/q}.$$

Proof.   We shall first prove that $a^p > b^p$ (for any positive integer p). The proof will be by induction.   By hypothesis, $a^1 > b^1$.   Suppose that $a^n > b^n$, n being any positive integer.   If it then follows that $a^{n+1} > b^{n+1}$, the Principle of Finite Induction guarantees that $a^p > b^p$ for all positive integers p.   Now, if $a^n > b^n$, Theorem 5 in conjunction with the hypothesis $a > b$ yields the conclusion that $a^{n+1} > b^{n+1}$.   This completes the first stage of the proof.

We now show that $a^{p/q} > b^{p/q}$.   Suppose that this is false, namely by Theorem 1 that $a^{p/q} \leq b^{p/q}$.   Then by what was just proved (with $a^{p/q}$ taking the rôle of b, $b^{p/q}$ taking the rôle of a, and q taking the rôle of p), it is clear that

$$a^p \leq b^p.$$

Since we have already proved that $a^p > b^p$, Theorem 1 says that this is a contradiction.   Thus the hypothesis $a^{p/q} \leq b^{p/q}$ is untenable; and by Theorem 1, $a^{p/q} > b^{p/q}$. ∎

With these fundamental rules in mind, one can develop many meaningful and beautiful inequalities.   But before proceeding to this task, let us consider some simple illustrations of the above theorems.

Example.   Show that $\sqrt{10} + \sqrt{2} > \sqrt{17}$.

Demonstration.   If the above inequality is true, then all of the following statements must be true:

$$10 + 2\sqrt{10}\,\sqrt{2} + 2 > 17 \qquad \text{(by Theorem 6 with } p = 2, q = 1)$$

$$2\sqrt{10}\,\sqrt{2} > 5 \qquad \text{(by Theorem 3)}$$

$$4 \cdot 10 \cdot 2 > 25 \qquad \text{(by Theorem 6 with } p = 2, q = 1).$$

But 80 *is* greater than 5 (we proved that $55 > 0$). Therefore,

$$2\sqrt{10}\,\sqrt{2} > 5 \qquad \text{(by Theorem 5 with } p = 1,\ q = 2)$$

$$10 + 2\sqrt{10}\,\sqrt{2} + 2 > 17 \qquad \text{(by Theorem 3)}$$

$$\sqrt{10} + \sqrt{2} > \sqrt{17} \qquad \text{(by Theorem 6 with } p = 1,\ q = 2).$$

Note that just because the truth of the desired conclusion implied that $80 > 25$, which is true, we could not then legitimately conclude that our desired inequality was valid. This is because of the fact that both true and false statements may be derived from a false statement. For example, consider the statement: $3 > 4$ and $1 > -1$. From this statement it follows by Theorem 4 with $c = 3$ that $9 > 12$ and by Theorem 3 that $4 > 3$.

An inequality which is slightly more sophisticated is

$$\frac{1}{\sqrt{4n+1}} < \frac{1}{2} \cdot \frac{3}{4} \cdot \frac{5}{6} \cdot \cdots \cdot \frac{2n-3}{2n-2} \cdot \frac{2n-1}{2n} < \frac{1}{\sqrt{3n+1}}$$

$(n = 2, 3, 4, \cdots)$.

We shall establish this inequality by using the Principle of Finite Induction. Clearly,

$$\frac{1}{\sqrt{4\cdot 2 + 1}} = \frac{1}{3} < \frac{1\cdot 3}{2\cdot 4} < \frac{1}{\sqrt{7}} = \frac{1}{\sqrt{3\cdot 2 + 1}} \qquad \text{(Theorems 4 and 6).}$$

The desired inequality is therefore true if $n = 2$. Suppose that it is true for a positive integer $n \geq 2$. If it can then be shown that it is true for $n + 1$, that is, that

$$\frac{1}{\sqrt{4n+5}} < \frac{1\cdot 3 \cdot \cdots \cdot (2n-1)(2n+1)}{2\cdot 4 \cdot \cdots \cdot 2n(2n+2)} < \frac{1}{\sqrt{3n+4}},$$

the desired result will have been obtained. By Theorems 2 and 4, this will be true if

(a) $$\frac{1}{\sqrt{4n+1}} \cdot \frac{2n+1}{2n+2} > \frac{1}{\sqrt{4n+5}}$$

and

(b) $$\frac{1}{\sqrt{3n+1}} \cdot \frac{2n+1}{2n+2} < \frac{1}{\sqrt{3n+4}}.$$

If (a) is true, then by Theorem 6 with $p = 2$ and $q = 1$, one finds that

$$\left(\frac{2n+1}{2n+2}\right)^2 \frac{1}{4n+1} > \frac{1}{4n+5},$$

or, by Theorem 4, that

$$(2n+1)^2(4n+5) > (2n+2)^2(4n+1).$$

Performing the indicated multiplications, one finds by Theorem 3 that the last inequality is equivalent to the result

$$16n^3 + 36n^2 + 24n + 5 > 16n^3 + 36n^2 + 24n + 4$$

or

$$1 > 0.$$

This reasoning may now be reversed and (a) thereby established. The proof of (b) is similar.

Can you improve this result?

For the sake of brevity, we shall not always specifically refer to Theorems 1–6 in future arguments where they are used. But the reader should recognize the fact that they are tacitly employed over and over again.

EXERCISES

1. Which is larger, 3 or $10 - 4\sqrt{3}$? Give a proof.
2. Show that $\sqrt[3]{5} < \sqrt{2} + 0.3$.
3. Which is greater, $a^2 + b^2 - ab$ or ab? Give a proof.
4. If m and n are positive integers, show that $\sqrt{2}$ lies between m/n and $(m + 2n)/(m + n)$.
5. Show that

$$1,998 < \sum_1^{10^6} \frac{1}{\sqrt{n}} < 1,999.$$

(Recall that $\displaystyle\sum_1^{10^6} \frac{1}{\sqrt{n}} = 1 + \frac{1}{\sqrt{2}} + \frac{1}{\sqrt{3}} + \cdots + \frac{1}{\sqrt{10^6}}$.)

HINT: First establish the inequality

$$2(\sqrt{n+1} - \sqrt{n}) < \frac{1}{\sqrt{n}} < 2(\sqrt{n} - \sqrt{n-1}), \quad n = 1, 2, 3, \cdots.$$

6. Prove that

$$1800 < \sum_{10^4}^{10^6} \frac{1}{\sqrt{n}} < 1800.02.$$

2. Conditional Inequalities

An inequality involving n real variables is said to be *conditional* if it does not hold over all of Euclidian n-space, the entire range of the variables. For example, if x and y are real variables, the inequalities

$$x < 3 \quad \text{and} \quad x + y > 1$$

are conditional inequalities, while

$$x^2 > -1 \quad \text{and} \quad x^2 + y^2 > -1$$

are not conditional inequalities since they hold for all real numbers x and y. This concept corresponds to the distinction made between conditional equations and identities in algebra:

$$x^2 - 2x + 1 = 0$$

is a conditional equation, while

$$(x - 1)^2 = x^2 - 2x + 1$$

is an identity.

Another important concept in the theory of inequalities, just as in other branches of mathematics, is that of absolute value.

Definition 2. The absolute value $|x|$ of a real number x is defined as follows:

$$|x| = x, \quad \text{if } x \geqq 0$$

$$|x| = -x, \quad \text{if } x < 0.$$

Thus, $|x|$ is the distance from the point x on the real line to the origin. Note that

$$|x^2| = |x|^2$$

and

$$\sqrt{x^2} = |x|;$$

for example, $\sqrt{(-3)^2} = 3$. For real numbers x and y, $|x - y|$ is the distance between x and y.

Let us now consider some specific conditional inequalities and their geometric interpretations.

(a) $|x - \pi| < 3$. This inequality is fulfilled by all points x on the open interval $(\pi - 3, \pi + 3)$ and only by these points (Fig. 2).

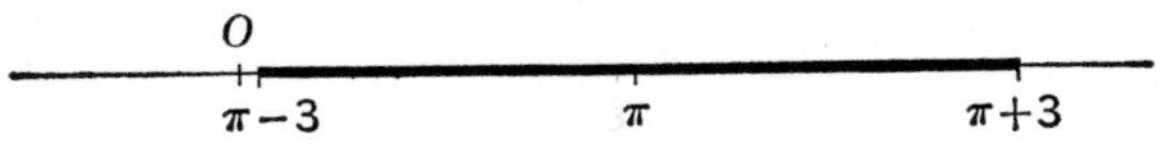

FIGURE 2

(b) $|x - \pi| < |x + \sqrt{2}|$. Any real number fulfilling this inequality must be such that it is closer to π than to $-\sqrt{2}$; that is, x must satisfy the inequality (Fig. 3)

$$x > \frac{\pi - \sqrt{2}}{2}.$$

Conversely, any real number satisfying the latter inequality satisfies the former inequality.

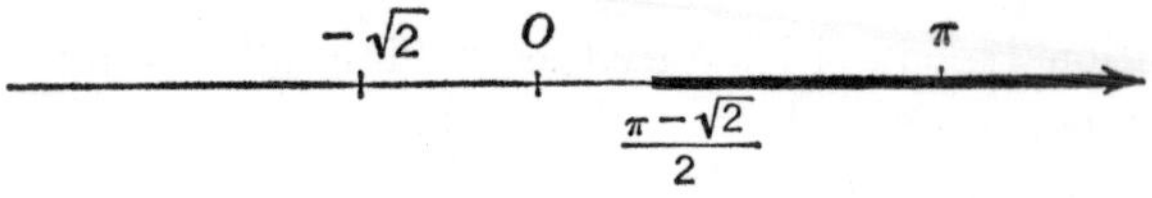

$$-\sqrt{2} \qquad O \qquad\qquad\qquad \pi$$

$$\frac{\pi - \sqrt{2}}{2}$$

FIGURE 3

(c) $|x + 2| + |x - 2| < 5$. This inequality is equivalent to the two inequalities

$$-\frac{5}{2} < x < \frac{5}{2}.$$

In order to prove this, consider the following three cases. If $x \geqq 2$, $|x + 2| + |x - 2| = (x + 2) + (x - 2)$. Thus, when $x \geqq 2$, $|x + 2| + |x - 2| < 5$ if and only if $2 \leqq x \leqq \frac{5}{2}$. If $-2 \leqq x \leqq 2$, $|x + 2| + |x - 2| = x + 2 - (x - 2)$ and hence is always less than 5. Finally, if $x \leqq -2$, $|x + 2| + |x - 2| = -(x + 2) - (x - 2)$; and consequently when $x \leqq -2$, $|x + 2| + |x - 2| < 5$ if and only if $-2 \geqq x > \frac{5}{2}$ (Fig. 4).

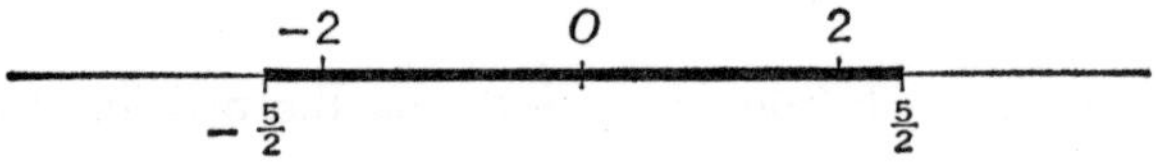

$$-2 \qquad\qquad O \qquad\qquad 2$$
$$-\frac{5}{2} \qquad\qquad\qquad\qquad \frac{5}{2}$$

FIGURE 4

The inequality $(x + 2) + (x - 2) < 5$, however, is satisfied on a half-line, namely for $x < \frac{5}{2}$.

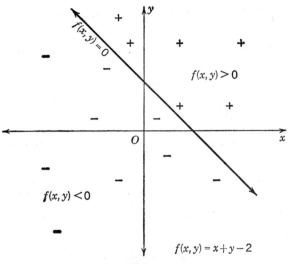

FIGURE 5

If f is a continuous real-valued function defined on some set D of the (x,y)-plane, the set of points of D where $f(x,y) = 0$ may describe a curve C in D. The set C often divides D into a number of subsets, throughout each of which one of the inequalities $f(x,y) < 0$ and $f(x,y) > 0$ holds. In the following examples, D will be the (x,y)-plane.

(d) If f is a linear function, that is, if $f(x,y) = ax + by + c$ $(a^2 + b^2 \neq 0)$, then the regions where $f(x,y) > 0$ and $f(x,y) < 0$ are half-planes whose common boundary is the graph of $f(x,y) = 0$ (Fig. 5).

(e) If $f(x,y) = x^2 + y^2 - 4$, then the region where $f(x,y) < 0$ is the interior of the circle with center at the point $(0,0)$ and radius 2.

(f) Let $f(x,y) = y - |x|$. The set of points (x,y) where $y - |x| > 0$ is the v-shaped region shown in Figure 6. It is bounded by the lines with the equations $y = x$ and $y = -x$. We see this by observing that if $x \geq 0$, $y - |x| = y - x$ and if $x < 0$, $y - |x| = y + x$.

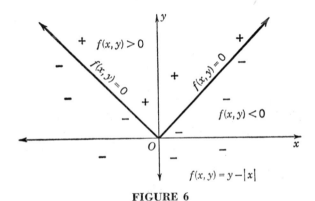

FIGURE 6

(g) $|x| + 2|y| < 3$. To determine the region where this inequality is satisfied, we first find its boundary, the set where $|x| + 2|y| = 3$. It is convenient to proceed case by case. If $x \geq 0$ and $y \geq 0$, then $|x| + 2|y| = x + 2y$. Therefore, that part of the line with equation $x + 2y = 3$ which lies in the first quadrant is part of the boundary of the region we seek. If $x \leq 0$ and $y \geq 0$, then $|x| + 2|y| = -x + 2y$. Thus, the segment of the line with equation $-x + 2y = 3$ which lies in the second quadrant is part of the boundary. Proceeding in this way, we find that the region is the interior of the parallelogram illustrated in Figure 7.

(h) The set of points (x,y) such that $f(x,y) = 0$ is not always a curve. For example, let f be the function 0, or the function $x^2 + y^2 + 1$.

(i) If $f(x,y) = (x^2 + y^2 - 4)(x^2 + 9y^2 - 9)$, then the set of points where $f(x,y) > 0$ consists of two separate regions: the region whose points lie inside both the ellipse with equation $x^2 + 9y^2 = 9$ and the circle with equation $x^2 + y^2 = 4$, and the region whose points lie outside both the circle and the ellipse.

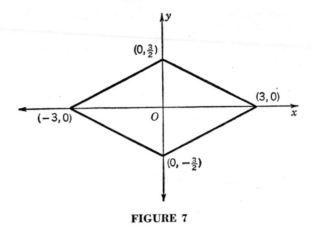

FIGURE 7

If z is a complex number, $z = x + iy$ (x and y real), then the absolute value $|z|$ of z is defined to be $\sqrt{x^2 + y^2}$. Note that

$$|z|^2 = z\bar{z} = (x + iy)(x - iy).$$

The numbers x and y are called the *real part* and the *imaginary part* of z, respectively; $\bar{z}$ is the *conjugate* of z. If z and w are complex numbers, then $|w - z|$ (or $|z - w|$) is the distance between w and z in the complex plane.

Consider the triangle with vertices the origin, w, and z. The lengths of its sides are $|w|$, $|z|$, and $|w - z|$. Thus the geometric theorem that the

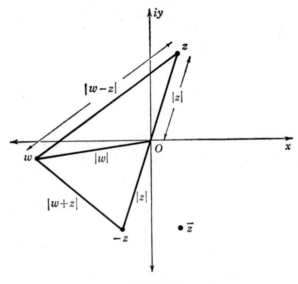

FIGURE 8

sum of the lengths of two sides of a triangle is greater than the length of the third side implies the inequality

$$|w - z| \leq |w| + |z|,$$

or equally well,

$$|w + z| \leq |w| + |z|.$$

For this reason the last inequality is called the *triangle inequality*. When does equality hold?

We can also establish the triangle inequality apart from geometric considerations.

Proof. First note that

$$|w + z|^2 = (w + z)(\bar{w} + \bar{z})$$
$$= |w|^2 + |z|^2 + (w\bar{z} + z\bar{w}).$$

Now, $w\bar{z} + z\bar{w}$ is real since $z\bar{w}$ is the conjugate of the complex number $w\bar{z}$. We shall show that

(*) $$w\bar{z} + z\bar{w} \leq 2|w| \cdot |z|.$$

If this is so, then

$$|w + z|^2 \leq |w|^2 + 2|w| \cdot |z| + |z|^2;$$

and by Theorem 6,

$$|w + z| \leq |w| + |z|.$$

In order to prove (*), observe that

$$(w\bar{z} - z\bar{w})^2 \leq 0.$$

This is true because $w\bar{z} - z\bar{w}$ is i times twice the imaginary part of $w\bar{z}$. Therefore, since

$$(w\bar{z} + z\bar{w})^2 = (w\bar{z} - z\bar{w})^2 + 4|w|^2 \cdot |z|^2,$$

we conclude that

$$w\bar{z} + z\bar{w} \leq 2|w| \cdot |z|.$$

Equality holds if and only if
$$w\bar{z} = z\bar{w} \quad \text{and} \quad w\bar{z} + z\bar{w} \geq 0.$$

This occurs if and only if $vx = uy$ and $ux \geq 0$ ($w = u + iv$). The geometric significance should be obvious from Figure 9.

The inequality

$$|w| - |z| \leq |w - z|$$

is implied by the theorem that the difference between the lengths of two sides of a triangle is less than the length of the third side.

In the remaining examples, w and z denote complex numbers.

(j) The inequality $|z| < 3$ holds in the interior of the circle with center at the origin and radius 3, and nowhere else.

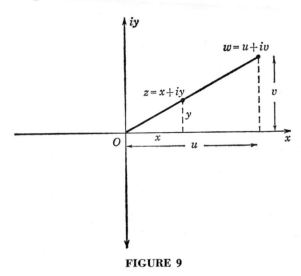

FIGURE 9

(k) The simultaneous inequalities $1 < |z| < 3$ hold only in the interior of the annulus bounded by the circles of radii 1 and 3 and with centers at the origin (Fig. 10).

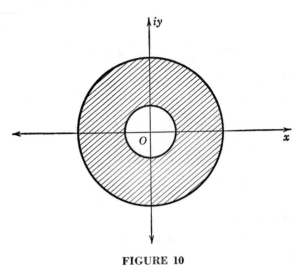

FIGURE 10

(l) The inequality $|z - 1| + |z + 1| < 4$ holds in the interior of an ellipse with foci at the points ± 1 and with semi-major axis of length 2, and nowhere else.

(m) A lemniscate is the locus of points the product of whose distances to two fixed points is a constant. Thus, the inequality $|z - 1| \cdot |z + 1| < 1$ (or $|z^2 - 1| < 1$) holds only in the interior of the lemniscate illustrated in Figure 11.

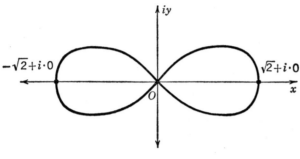

FIGURE 11

The inequality $|z^2 - 4| < 1$ holds if and only if z lies in one of the two disjoint regions bounded by the lemniscate with equation $|z^2 - 4| = 1$ (Fig. 12).

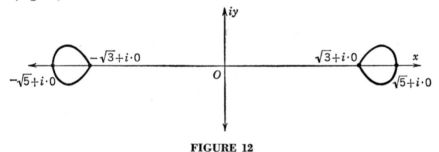

FIGURE 12

EXERCISES AND PROBLEMS

1. For what real numbers x is
  (a) $4 - x < 3 - 2x$,
  (b) $4x^2 - 13x + 3 < 0$,
  (c) $x^2 + 4x + 4x > 0$,
  (d) $(x - 1)(x - 2)(x - 3)(x - 4) \geq 0$,
  (e) $x(x - 1)(x - 2)(x - 3) < 0$,
  (f) $(\frac{1}{2})^x < 10$?

2. Describe and illustrate the regions in the (x,y)-plane for which
  (a) $2x^2 + 7y \leq 15y + 8$,
  (b) $x^2 - xy + y^2 \leq 0$,
  (c) $4x^2 + y^2 > 1$,
  (d) $\dfrac{2x - 1}{3 - 2y} < 3$,

(e) $x^2 - 2|y| > 2,$

(f) $|x| + |y| < 1,$

(g) $|x - y| + 4 < |x|,$

(h) $|x - 1| + |y - 1| \geqq 2,$

(i) $|x| \cdot |y| < 4,$

(j) $|3x| + |2y| < 5,$

(k) $|x + y|^2 - |x - y|^2 > 1,$

(l) $[1 + (x + y)]^{1/2} > x + y.$

3. Let z be a complex variable. In what regions is
   (a) $|z| - |z + 1| < 4,$

   (b) $|z| < 2|z - 1|,$

   (c) $|z^2 + 9| < 1?$

4. Let v, w, and z be any three complex numbers. Show that

$$|v| + |v + w| + |w + z| + |2 + z| \geqq 2.$$

5. Give a nongeometric proof of the inequality

$$|w| - |z| < |w + z|.$$

When does equality hold?

[2]

Two Ancient Theorems

3.   Geometric and Arithmetic Means

One of the early triumphs of the calculus was the solution of a large class of problems involving maxima and minima by means of a single receipt.   Before the "invention" of the calculus by Newton and Leibnitz, many problems of this kind had been solved, and their solution made others all the more tantalizing.   For example, solutions of simple isoperimetric problems were known (*iso* means *same*): Of all triangles with the same perimeter, which has the greatest area; of all isoperimetric rectangles, which has the greatest area?   At the same time, problems such as finding that curve joining two points down which a ball would roll the fastest (the curve of quickest descent), or determining which box among all those that can be inscribed in a given ellipsoid has the greatest volume, could not be solved with existing methods.   On the other hand, some extremal problems whose solution by means of calculus is either cumbersome or impossible to carry out can be solved with the aid of more elementary methods. A discussion of some of these elementary methods is useful for two reasons: it provides motivation for and better understanding of the calculus; and it demonstrates that if the receipts of calculus fail, all is not necessarily lost.   This section is devoted to an examination of one elementary tool for the solution of extremal problems: the Theorem of Arithmetic and Geometric Means.   We shall see what the theorem means, whence it comes, and how it is used.

Let ABC (Fig. 13) be a right triangle with hypotenuse AB and altitude $\overline{CD} = x$.   Then, since the triangles ACD and BCD are similar,

$$\frac{a}{x} = \frac{x}{b}.$$

The number x is called the *geometric mean* of a and b.   Note that if $a < b$, then $a < x < b$.   Another way of defining x is to say that it is the length of a side of a square whose area is equal to that of a rectangle with sides of lengths a and b.   This definition comes from ancient Greece and can be found in Euclid's *Elements*.

15

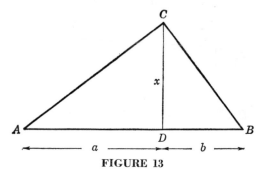

FIGURE 13

Definition 3. The geometric mean G_n of n positive numbers $x_1, \cdots, x_n$ is the nth root of their product:

$$G_n = (x_1 \cdot x_2 \cdot \cdots \cdot x_n)^{1/n} \equiv \left(\prod_1^n x_i \right)^{1/n}.$$

Thus, G_n is the length of an edge of an n-dimensional cube whose volume is equal to that of an n-dimensional rectangular parallelepiped whose orthogonal (mutually perpendicular) edges have lengths $x_1, \cdots, x_n$.

The definition of an arithmetic mean is more familiar.

Definition 4. The arithmetic mean A_n of n numbers $x_1, \cdots, x_n$ is one nth of their sum:

$$A_n = \frac{\sum\limits_1^n x_i}{n}.$$

Arithmetic and geometric means are used in making estimates or approximations. It is often more convenient to speak of the mean of several quantities rather than to speak of each of them individually. Information provided by data (for example, weather data) is more easily grasped in this way. The question naturally arises, then, what the relation may be, if any, between the arithmetic and geometric means of the same set of n positive numbers. A hint as to the answer is provided by the following observation.

It is geometrically obvious that among all possible right triangles with hypotenuse AB, the isosceles triangle has the greatest altitude. For the isosceles triangle (Fig. 13)

$$x = \frac{(a + b)}{2}.$$

But $a + b$ is fixed. Hence, for any other right triangle on the hypotenuse AB

$$\sqrt{ab} = x < \frac{a + b}{2}.$$

Therefore, if a and b are any two positive numbers,

$$\sqrt{ab} \leqq \frac{a+b}{2}.$$

It is easy to confirm this inequality analytically by means of Theorem 6: the inequality

$$(a-b)^2 \geqq 0$$

implies that

$$a^2 + 2ab + b^2 \geqq 4ab,$$

or

$$\left(\frac{a+b}{2}\right)^2 \geqq ab,$$

from which it follows by Theorem 6 that

$$\frac{a+b}{2} \geqq \sqrt{ab}.$$

Equality holds if and only if $a = b$.

This inequality has yet another geometric interpretation: among the class of all rectangles with the same perimeter P, the square has the largest area. For let the sides of such a rectangle have lengths a and b. Then $P = 2(a+b)$, and we may rewrite the last inequality in the form

$$ab \leqq \left(\frac{P}{4}\right)^2.$$

Equality holds if and only if $a = b = P/4$.

The inequality may be interpreted in still a different fashion: of all rectangles with area A, the square has the least perimeter. For, denoting the lengths of the sides of any such rectangle by a and b, we see that

$$\frac{P}{4} = \frac{a+b}{2} \geqq \sqrt{ab} = A^{1/2},$$

or

$$P \geqq 4A^{1/2}.$$

Equality holds if and only if $a = b$. This result was known before the time of Euclid.

On the basis of these observations it is natural to ask whether it is always true that $G_n \leqq A_n$. The answer to this question is contained in the following celebrated theorem.

Theorem 7. (*The Theorem of Arithmetic and Geometric Means*). The geometric mean of n positive real numbers is always less than or equal to their arithmetic mean; equality holds if and only if the numbers are all equal.

Before we attempt to prove this theorem, let us look at some geometric interpretations of it and judge their plausibility. Let the lengths of the orthogonal edges of an n-dimensional box be $x_1, \cdots, x_n$, let its volume be V, and let the sum of the lengths of its edges be P. Theorem 7 implies that

$$V^{1/n} = G_n \leqq A_n = \frac{P}{2^{n-1}n},$$

or

$$V \leqq \left[\frac{P}{2^{n-1}n} \right]^n.$$

Equality holds if and only if $x_1 = x_2 = \cdots = x_n$. Thus if P is fixed, V is greatest when $x_1 = \cdots = x_n$. Geometrically, this means that of all n-dimensional boxes ("rectangular parallelepipeds") with the same sum P of the lengths of their edges, the "cube" has the greatest volume. Moreover, of all n-dimensional boxes with the same volume, the cube has the least sum of all edges. These two theorems are plausible generalizations of the previous statements about rectangles. Further, if one considers various choices of n and specific numbers x_i, one finds that G_n is indeed never greater than A_n. (Try it; examples are one kind of experiment in mathematics.)

It remains to give a proof of Theorem 7. The following elegant one is due to the nineteenth century French mathematician Augustin Cauchy (1789–1857).

One Proof of Theorem 7. Cauchy observed that if one could just show that $G_n \leqq A_n$ whenever n is a power of 2, then one could prove the theorem for all other n. He also found a simple way to prove the theorem for $n = 2^k$, $k = 1, 2, 3, \cdots$. Here is his reasoning.

Cauchy used induction to prove the theorem for n a power of 2. If $n = 2$, that is, $k = 1$, it is clear that

$$x_1 x_2 = \left(\frac{x_1 + x_2}{2} \right)^2 - \left(\frac{x_1 - x_2}{2} \right)^2$$

so that by Definition 1,

$$x_1 x_2 \leqq \left(\frac{x_1 + x_2}{2} \right)^2.$$

Equality holds if and only if $(x_1 - x_2)^2 = 0$, that is, if and only if $x_1 = x_2$. If $n = 4$, that is, $k = 2$, one sees by four applications of this result that

$$(x_1 x_2)(x_3 x_4) \leqq \left(\frac{x_1 + x_2}{2} \right)^2 \left(\frac{x_3 + x_4}{2} \right)^2 \leqq \left(\frac{\sum_1^4 x_i}{4} \right)^4.$$

To obtain the last inequality, observe that

$$\left(\frac{x_1 + x_2}{2}\right)\left(\frac{x_3 + x_4}{2}\right) \leq \left[\frac{\dfrac{x_1 + x_2}{2} + \dfrac{x_3 + x_4}{2}}{2}\right]^2.$$

Now we make the hypothesis of induction, namely, that the inequality is true for $n = 2^k$; and we examine the truth of the inequality for $n = 2^{k+1}$. By the result for $n = 2^k$, we see that

$$\prod_1^{2^{k+1}} x_i = \left(\prod_1^{2^k} x_i\right)\left(\prod_{2^k+1}^{2^{k+1}} x_i\right) \leq \left(\frac{\sum_1^{2^k} x_i}{2^k}\right)^{2^k}\left(\frac{\sum_{2^k+1}^{2^{k+1}} x_i}{2^k}\right)^{2^k}.$$

But

$$\left(\frac{\sum_1^{2^k} x_i}{2^k}\right)\left(\frac{\sum_{2^k+1}^{2^{k+1}} x_i}{2^k}\right) \leq \left(\frac{\sum_1^{2^{k+1}} x_i}{2^{k+1}}\right)^2.$$

Therefore,

$$\prod_1^{2^{k+1}} x_i \leq \left(\frac{\sum_1^{2^{k+1}} x_i}{2^{k+1}}\right)^{2^{k+1}}.$$

By the Principle of Finite Induction and Theorem 6, it now follows that Theorem 7 is true for n a positive power of 2.

If n is not a power of 2, let 2^m be a power of 2 greater than n, and let $2^m - n = k$. Then by Theorem 7 as applied to the 2^m numbers

$$x_1, \cdots, x_n, \underbrace{A_n, \cdots, A_n,}_{k \text{ terms}}$$

$$\left(\prod_1^n x_i\right) A_n^k \leq \left[\frac{\sum_1^n x_i + kA_n}{2^m}\right]^{2^m} = \left[\frac{nA_n + kA_n}{2^m}\right]^{2^m} = A_n^{2^m},$$

or

$$G_n^m A_n^k \leq A_n^{2^m}.$$

Consequently,

$$G_n^n \leq A_n^n.$$

Again by Theorem 6, the inequality is equivalent to

$$G_n \leq A_n.$$

Of course, equality holds in every instance above if and only if $x_1 = \cdots = x_n$.∎

This proof has two important features: it is short and clear, and it is brilliant. One wonders how Cauchy ever thought of proving the theorem in this unexpected way. While one can possibly discover a reasonable motivation for Cauchy's proof, it is good to realize that brilliance often needs no explanation. On the other hand, it is excellent training to try to arrive constructively at a proof of a theorem without a stroke of brilliance, since most of us must always proceed in this way if we are to proceed at all. To do this with respect to Theorem 7, we first observe, as we essentially did above in interpreting the theorem geometrically, that the following theorem is equivalent to Theorem 7.

Theorem 8. The product of n positive numbers whose sum is fixed is greatest when they are all equal.

This proposition suggests that if two sets of n positive numbers have the same sum S, the one whose members are "more nearly" equal to S/n has the greater product of its elements. The question is to make the notion of "more nearly" precise. Given a set of n numbers whose sum is S and not all of whose members are equal, there must be one member smaller than S/n and one larger. If we increase the size of a smaller one and correspondingly decrease the size of a larger one, then it is reasonable to hope that the new set of n numbers has a larger product. This turns out to be true. However, how shall we ever obtain in this way a set of n numbers with sum S whose product we cannot increase any more? The key to this problem lies in our conjecture that this unimprovable set must consist of n equal numbers. We must so change the original numbers that one by one they are made equal to S/n. Let us now transform this hazy outline into a solid proof.

Proof of Theorem 8. Given n positive numbers with sum S, we are to prove their product must be less than or equal to $(S/n)^n$. If the numbers are all equal to their arithmetic mean S/n, then clearly equality holds. Otherwise, there must be at least one smaller than $A_n = S/n$ and at least one larger. Choose one which is smaller and one which is larger, and call them a_1 and a_2, respectively. Then

$$a_1 = A_n - h \quad \text{and} \quad a_2 = A_n + k$$

where h and k are positive. Next choose $a_1' = A_n$ and $a_2' = A_n + k - h$, and consider the product $a_1' a_2'$. Clearly,

$$a_1' a_2' = A_n(A_n + k - h)$$
$$= (A_n^2 + kA_n - hA_n),$$

while

$$a_1 a_2 = (A_n - h)(A_n + k)$$
$$= (A_n^2 + kA_n - hA_n) - hk.$$

The product hk is positive, and

$$a_1'a_2' = a_1a_2 + hk.$$

Therefore,

$$a_1'a_2' > a_1a_2.$$

Of course, by deliberate choice $a_1' + a_2' = a_1 + a_2$. Thus, the set of n numbers consisting of a_1', a_2' and the unchosen $n - 2$ numbers of the given set has sum S but a greater product than the product of the numbers of the original set.

If the numbers in the new set are all equal, then it must be that the product of those in the given set is less than A_n^n. Otherwise, there must be at least one number of the new set smaller than A_n and at least one larger. Pick one of each kind, and repeat the previous argument. It is clear that after at most $n - 1$ steps of this sort we shall have constructed a set of n identical numbers with sum S and such that the product of the members of this set is greater than the product of the original n numbers.∎

4. An Application

The next theorem is an application of Theorem 7 which is useful in the solution of a number of problems. In particular, we shall use it to answer the familiar question: Which right circular cylinder has the least surface area among all those with the same volume? The Binomial Theorem tells us that when n is a positive integer

$$(1 + x)^n = 1 + nx + \sum_2^n \frac{n!}{k!(n - k)!} x^k.$$

If $x > 0$, then since each coefficient

$$\frac{n!}{k!(n - k)!} \quad (k = 2, \cdots, n)$$

is a positive integer, we see that

$$(1 + x)^n > 1 + nx.$$

Theorem 9 gives a generalization of this inequality.

Theorem 9. If $x \geq -1$ and $0 < \alpha < 1$, then

(1) $$(1 + x)^\alpha \leq 1 + \alpha x.$$

If $\alpha < 0$ or $\alpha > 1$ and $x \geq -1$, then

(2) $$(1 + x)^\alpha \geq 1 + \alpha x.$$

Equality holds in these inequalities if and only if $x = 0$.

Proof. We shall give a proof only for α rational. Suppose that $\alpha = m/n$ and $0 < \alpha < 1$, where m and n are positive integers. In order to be able to apply Theorem 7, we write $(1 + x)^{m/n}$ as

$$\sqrt[n]{\underbrace{(1 + x) \cdots (1 + x)}_{m \text{ factors}} \underbrace{1 \cdot 1 \cdots 1}_{n-m \text{ factors}}}.$$

We can then conclude that

$$(1 + x)^{m/n} \leqq \frac{m(1 + x) + n - m}{n} = 1 + \frac{m}{n} x.$$

Equality holds if and only if $1 + x = 1$, that is, only if $x = 0$.

We next examine the case $\alpha > 1$. If $(1 + \alpha x)$ is negative, inequality (2) clearly holds. If $1 + \alpha x \geq 0$, then $\alpha x \geq -1$; and by the inequality (1),

$$(1 + \alpha x)^{1/\alpha} \leqq 1 + \frac{1}{\alpha} \cdot \alpha x = 1 + x,$$

since $0 < \dfrac{1}{\alpha} < 1$. Thus, by Theorem 6,

$$(1 + \alpha x) \leqq (1 + x)^{\alpha}.$$

Equality holds if and only if $\alpha x = 0$, that is, if and only if $x = 0$.

The case $\alpha < 0$ remains. If $1 + \alpha x$ is also negative, then inequality (2) is obvious. If $1 + \alpha x \geq 0$, we choose a positive integer n such that $0 < -\alpha/n < 1$; and we consider the quantity

$$[(1 + x)^{\alpha}]^{-1/n} \quad \text{or, what is the same,} \quad (1 + x)^{-\alpha/n}.$$

Then by (1),

$$(1 + x)^{-\alpha/n} \leqq 1 - \frac{\alpha}{n} x.$$

Therefore,

$$(1 + x)^{\alpha/n} \geqq \frac{1}{1 - \dfrac{\alpha}{n} x}.$$

But

$$\frac{1}{1 - \dfrac{\alpha}{n} x} = \frac{1 + \dfrac{\alpha}{n} x}{\left(1 - \dfrac{\alpha}{n} x\right)\left(1 + \dfrac{\alpha}{n} x\right)},$$

$$= \frac{1 + \dfrac{\alpha}{n} x}{1 - \left(\dfrac{\alpha x}{n}\right)^2},$$

$$\geqq 1 + \frac{\alpha}{n} x.$$

Thus,

$$(1+x)^{\alpha/n} \geq 1 + \frac{\alpha}{n}x, \quad \text{or} \quad (1+x)^\alpha \geq \left(1 + \frac{\alpha}{n}x\right)^n.$$

Let us now choose n so great that $\alpha x/n \geq -1$. Then, by what we have already proved (the case $\alpha > 1$ and $x \geq -1$ with $\alpha = n$), we conclude that

$$(1+x)^\alpha \geq \left(1 + \frac{\alpha}{n}x\right)^n \geq 1 + n \cdot \frac{\alpha x}{n} = 1 + \alpha x.$$

It is easy to see that equality holds only if $x = 0$.∎

If we replace x by $y - 1$, then (1) and (2) take the form

(1′) $y^\alpha - \alpha y \leq 1 - \alpha$ (if $y \geq 0$ and $0 < \alpha < 1$),

(2′) $y^\alpha - \alpha y \geq 1 - \alpha$ (if $y \geq 0$ and $\alpha > 1$ or $\alpha < 0$).

Equality holds in either (1′) or (2′) only if $y = 1$.

The inequality (2′) yields the solution of the above mentioned problem: What right circular cylinder of volume V has the least surface area S? Suppose such a cylinder is given with radius r and height h. Then

$$V = \pi r^2 h \quad \text{and} \quad S = 2\pi(r^2 + rh).$$

Substituting the value of h in terms of r and V for h in the expression for S, we find

$$S = 2\pi\left(r^2 + \frac{V}{\pi r}\right).$$

The sum in the parentheses resembles $y^\alpha - \alpha y$ with $y = 1/r$ and $\alpha = -2$, except that the coefficient of $1/r$ is V/π and not 2. We need only to determine the ratio of r to h, since all right circular cylinders with a given ratio of r to h are similar. Hence, we lose no generality if we suppose that $V = 2\pi$. In this circumstance,

$$S = 2\pi\left(r^2 + \frac{2}{r}\right).$$

By (2′), the minimum value of S occurs when

$$y = \frac{1}{r} = 1.$$

Thus, for S a minimum we must have

$$V = 2\pi = \pi h, \quad \text{or} \quad h = 2.$$

We have therefore proved that the right circular cylinder with volume V which has the least surface area has a diameter equal to its altitude. Theorem 9 may also be used to solve the following problems.

PROBLEMS

1. What is the box (without a top) of largest volume which can be constructed from a square piece of tin of edge length $2a$ by cutting a square from each corner and folding up the edges? (See Fig. 14.)

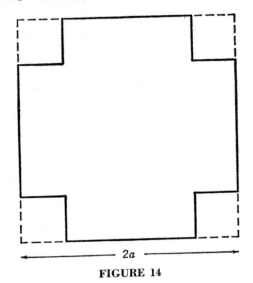

$$\longleftarrow \quad 2a \quad \longrightarrow$$

FIGURE 14

2. Find the minimum values of $x^3 - 27x$ and $x^{-1/3} + 27x$ for $x > 0$.

3. Prove that if $\alpha > 0$, then

$$\frac{n^{\alpha+1}}{\alpha+1} < \sum_1^n k^\alpha < \frac{(n+1)^{\alpha+1}}{\alpha+1}.$$

4. Prove that for $-1 < \alpha < 0$,

$$\frac{(n+1)^{\alpha+1}}{\alpha+1} < \sum_1^n k^\alpha < \frac{n^{\alpha+1}}{\alpha+1}.$$

5. Find an upper bound for $\sum_1^n \frac{1}{k^p}$ $(p = 2, 3, \cdots)$.

FURTHER PROBLEMS

6. Write down a proof that Theorem 8 implies Theorem 7. HINT: Given n positive numbers $x_1, \cdots x_n$, in order to show that

$$\left(\prod_1^n x_i\right)^{1/n} \leqq \frac{\sum_1^n x_i}{n},$$

first consider the set of n numbers y_i $(i = 1, \cdots, n)$ where

$$y_i = \frac{x_i}{\sum\limits_{1}^{n} x_k} \, .$$

Then apply Theorem 8.

7. Prove that either one of Theorems 7 and 8 is equivalent to the following one:

Theorem 10. The sum of n positive numbers whose product is 1 is least when they are all equal.

Remember that to prove this equivalence you must prove two things: that Theorem 8 (or 7) implies Theorem 10 and conversely that Theorem 10 implies Theorem 8 (or 7).

8. Prove that of all three dimensional boxes with the same surface area, the cube has the greatest volume.

9. If x and y are positive, show that

$$(xy^n)^{1/(n+1)} < \frac{x + ny}{n + 1} \quad (n = 1, 2, \cdots),$$

unless $x = y$.

10. Prove that

$$n! < \left(\frac{n + 1}{2}\right)^n \quad (n = 2, 3, 4, \cdots).$$

11. Give more than one proof of the theorem that if $x_1, \cdots, x_n$ are positive, then

$$\left(\sum\limits_{1}^{n} x_i\right)\left(\sum\limits_{1}^{n} \frac{1}{x_i}\right) \geq n^2,$$

with equality holding if and only if $x_1 = x_2 = \cdots = x_n$.

12. Let ABC be a triangle with perimeter P and area T, and let

$$\overline{AB} = c, \quad \overline{AC} = b, \quad \text{and} \quad \overline{BC} = a.$$

Heron's formula states that

$$16T^2 = P(P - 2a)(P - 2b)(P - 2c).$$

You may more easily recognize it in the form

$$T = [s(s - a)(s - b)(s - c)]^{1/2},$$

where s is the semiperimeter $P/2$.

Theorem 11. Of all triangles having a common base and perimeter, the isosceles triangle has the greatest area.

Prove this theorem using Heron's formula and one of Theorems 7, 8, and 10.

13. Similarly prove

Theorem 12. Of all triangles with the same base and area, the isosceles triangle has the least perimeter.

14. Give analogous proofs of

> **Theorem 13.** Of all triangles with the same perimeter, the equilateral triangle has the greatest area,

and

> **Theorem 14.** Of all triangles with the same area, the equilateral triangle has the least perimeter.

15. Prove that Theorems 11 and 12 are equivalent. HINT: To prove that Theorem 11 implies Theorem 12 consider three triangles:

   (a) any triangle—suppose it has area T and perimeter P;
   (b) an isosceles triangle with the same base and area as triangle (a) but with perimeter P_1;
   (c) an isosceles triangle with the same base and perimeter as triangle (a) but with area T_2.

16. Prove that Theorems 13 and 14 are equivalent.

17. Of all triangles circumscribed about a given circle, which has the least area and which has the shortest perimeter? Prove your conjectures.

18. Let a "blank" be a name for some plane geometric figure, and suppose that all blanks are similar. Let C be any class of plane geometric figures. For example, a blank could be an equilateral triangle, and C could be the class of all triangles. Establish the equivalence of the following two theorems.

   (A) Of all figures in C which have perimeter P, the blank has the greatest area.
   (B) Of all figures in C which have area T, the blank has the least perimeter.

Mathematicians call theorems like (A) and (B) *dual* theorems. What you have just shown is that the theory of isoperimetric theorems in the plane exhibits duality, that is, that isoperimetric theorems come in equivalent pairs.

19. If Q is a quadrilateral with sides of lengths a, b, c, and d, a pair of opposite angles α and β, and area T (Fig. 15), then one can rather easily and simply show that

$$2T = ab \sin \alpha + cd \sin \beta$$

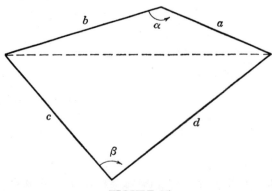

FIGURE 15

and

$$a^2 + b^2 - 2ab \cos \alpha = c^2 + d^2 - 2cd \cos \beta.$$

Derive the formula

$$16T^2 + (a^2 + b^2 - c^2 - d^2)^2 = 4a^2b^2 + 4c^2d^2 - 8abcd \cos (\alpha + \beta).$$

20. Theorem 15. Of all quadrilaterals with the same sides in the same order, the one which can be inscribed in a circle has the greatest area.

Prove this theorem.

21. Theorem 16. Of all quadrilaterals of perimeter P which may be inscribed in circles, the square has the greatest area.

Prove this theorem. HINT: First show that if the area of such a quadrilateral is T and the sides are of lengths a, b, c, and d, then

$$16T^2 = (P - 2a)(P - 2b)(P - 2c)(P - 2d).$$

5.   The Isoperimetric Theorem

Combining Theorems 15 and 16, one can conclude that

Of all isoperimetric plane quadrilaterals, the square has the greatest area.

However, no one has been able to give an analogous proof of the isoperimetric theorems for pentagons, hexagons, etc. The Isoperimetric Theorem is as follows.

Theorem 17. Of all plane figures with perimeter P, the circle has the greatest area.

We shall not give a proof of Theorem 17, or of Theorem 18 below, in this study. Theorem 17 is the most general isoperimetric theorem that can be stated for plane figures. It took mankind about two thousand years after discovering this theorem to prove it! Where does the difficulty lie? Well, it is easy to prove that if there actually does exist a plane figure of maximum area among all those with perimeter P, then it must be a circle. However, the "if," the question of existence of such a figure, is a difficult one to remove. It was not removed until the work of the German mathematician Karl Weierstrass, who was a professor at the University of Berlin in the last half of the nineteenth century. He was a founder and developer of the rigor which has become an essential feature of mathematics. Many mathematicians before him, including Archimedes, knew the Isoperimetric Theorem, and many thought that they had a proof. Weierstrass was the first to point out the possibility that a solution to a problem in maxima or minima may not exist. He not only raised the question, but he also answered it. He developed the calculus of variations on a rigorous basis, and he was then able to establish conditions under which one can assert the existence of solutions to problems involving maxima and minima.

The most elegant pseudo-proofs of the Isoperimetric Theorem were created by the brilliant Swiss geometer Jacob Steiner (1796–1863); in fact, his methods are still used in dealing with geometric problems. One of his "proofs" of the Isoperimetric Theorem is given below.

Definition 5. A set of points is said to be convex if the straight line segment joining any two points of the set also lies in the set.

A plane *convex body* or *figure* is any bounded plane convex set that is not a straight line segment. Circles, ellipses, triangles, and parallelograms are among the most commonly occurring plane convex bodies. The theory of convex bodies is a surprisingly beautiful and well-developed one. It contains an amazing number of useful theorems, and it finds application in almost every branch of pure and applied mathematics.

It is intuitively clear that every convex body has a boundary. The boundary may be described as follows: a point P is on the boundary of a convex body B if and only if every circle with center at P contains points of B *and* points outside of B. A straight line cuts the boundary of a convex body in at most two points. It is also intuitively clear that the boundary of a plane convex body has a finite length and that a plane convex body itself has a finite area. The boundary of a plane convex body is a simple closed curve, that is, the boundary can be continuously distorted into the circumference of a circle without two distinct points of it ever coalescing. All these statements can be rigorously proved, but we shall not investigate such delicate matters here.

An Argument of Steiner's. Let C be any plane figure of perimeter P. Clearly, if C is not convex, we can construct another figure of perimeter P and with a greater area:

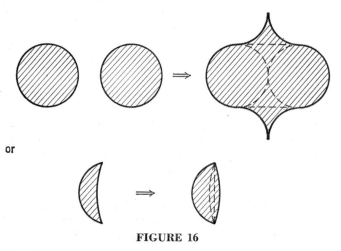

or

FIGURE 16

Further, if C is convex but is not a circle, we can again construct a figure with the same perimeter but with a larger area. To do this we use the isoperimetric theorem for quadrilaterals which you have proved above. If C is not a circle and is convex, then there must exist four points on its boundary which are not the vertices of a quadrilateral inscribed in a circle. Consider the parts of C which lie exterior to such a quadrilateral to be rigid and rigidly attached to its sides, and assume that its vertices are flexible joints (Fig. 17). If we now distort the quadrilateral into a new one which can be inscribed in a circle, the total area of the new one plus the attached pieces of C will be greater than the area of C, while the perimeter of the new figure will be P. (If there is some overlapping near the

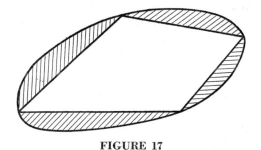

FIGURE 17

joints, pieces may be added so as to compensate for the lost area while at the same time preserving the perimeter.) Therefore, to any plane figure which is not a circle, there corresponds another of the same perimeter but with a greater area.

However, just because we can prove that any noncircular figure can be "improved," it does not follow that a figure of maximum area with a given perimeter does indeed exist. A. S. Besicovitch has proved, for example, that a straight line segment of unit length can be turned completely around inside a plane figure of arbitrarily small area! There is no figure of least area in which a line segment of unit length may be so moved as to end up turned around. [A. S. Besicovitch, "On Kakeya's problem and a similar one," *Mathematische Zeitschrift*, vol. 27, 1928.]

Let us now return to the subject of the isoperimetric theorem for n-gons:

Theorem 18. Of all n-gons with perimeter P, the regular n-gon has the greatest area $(n = 3, 4, \cdots)$.

There are several reasons for believing in the truth of this theorem. Firstly, we have already proved it for $n = 3$ and 4. Secondly, the conclusion is an attractive one—if any n-gon of perimeter P is to have the greatest area the regular one must surely be that one. Thirdly, one can prove that Theorem 17 implies Theorem 18.

PROBLEM

22. Prove that if Theorem 17 is correct, then so is Theorem 18.

It was remarked above that an elementary proof of Theorem 18 has not yet been found. The term "elementary proof" means here a proof that does not use the basic ideas used to prove Theorem 17. Moreover, it should be a constructive proof. (The proofs of Theorem 18 for $n = 3$ and 4 which we have given are constructive, not indirect.) Let us now examine some possible steps in a proof of Theorem 18.

Suppose an n-gon Q with perimeter P is given. If Q is not convex, then we can construct a convex n-gon Q' of perimeter P, and with greater area than Q, in the following way. If Q is not convex, it is because the line segments joining one or more pairs of nonconsecutive vertices of Q lie outside Q. To obtain Q' first replace the boundary of Q by the outer boundary of the polygon formed by Q and these line segments (Fig. 18).

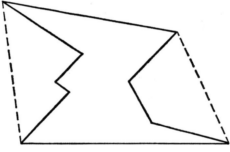

FIGURE 18

The resultant polygon H has an area greater than that of Q and a smaller perimeter. The boundary of H is called the *convex hull* of Q. We then construct Q': it is the polygon of perimeter P which is similar to H. There is one possible objection that may be raised to this reasoning: Q' may not be an n-gon but a k-gon with $k < n$. Mathematicians would say, however, that Q' is an n-gon, albeit a degenerate one. A mathematician would simply label $n - k$ points lying on the interior of a side of Q' as vertices of Q' so as to make n vertices in all. (In an attempt to overcome this objection in another, perhaps more honest, way one is led to Theorem 19 below.)

Definition 6. Let Q be the boundary of a nonconvex n-gon P. Let ab be a segment of the convex hull H of Q such that if x lies in both Q and ab, then x is either a or b. A *reflection operation* s on P reflects that piece of Q lying interior to H and having end points a and b in ab as a mirror (Fig. 19).

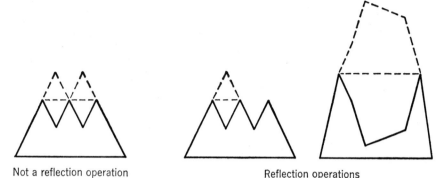

Not a reflection operation   Reflection operations

FIGURE 19

The new polygon $s(P)$ is a k-gon $(n - 2 \leq k \leq n)$ with sides congruent to corresponding sides of P. Consider a sequence $\{r_m(P)\}$ $(m = 0, 1, 2, \cdots)$, where $r_0(P) = P$ and $r_m(P) = r_m[r_{m-1}(P)]$ $(m > 0)$ and where the r_m's are arbitrarily chosen reflection operations.

Theorem 19. If P is a nonconvex n-gon, any sequence $\{r_m(P)\}$ is finite, and the last member is a convex k-gon $(k \leq n)$.

In order to prove this theorem, we need to use a fundamental property of the real number system which is known as the least upper bound property, and which we now describe.

Let an infinite sequence of real numbers $b_1, b_2, \cdots, b_n, b_{n+1}, \cdots$ be denoted $\{b_n\}$. For example,

$$\left\{\frac{1}{n}\right\} = \left\{1, \frac{1}{2}, \frac{1}{3}, \frac{1}{4}, \cdots, \frac{1}{n}, \frac{1}{n+1}, \cdots\right\};$$

$$\left\{\frac{n^3 + 1}{n^2}\right\} = \left\{2, \frac{9}{4}, \frac{28}{9}, \frac{65}{16}, \cdots, \frac{n^3 + 1}{n^2}, \cdots\right\}.$$

A number M is said to be an *upper bound* for the sequence $\{b_n\}$ if and only if

$$b_k \leq M \quad (k = 1, 2, 3, \cdots).$$

A number L is said to be a *lower bound* for the sequence b_n if and only if

$$L \leq b_k \quad (k = 1, 2, 3, \cdots).$$

The following theorem expresses the least upper bound property of the real number system.

Theorem. Every sequence of real numbers having an upper bound has a least upper bound, and every sequence of real numbers having a lower bound has a greatest lower bound.

If x is the least upper bound of $\{b_n\}$, we write $x = \text{l.u.b.}_n \, b_n$. For example,

$$1 = \text{l.u.b.}_n \frac{1}{n}, \quad \text{and} \quad 0 = \text{g.l.b.}_n \frac{1}{n}.$$

Now suppose that $\{b_n\}$ is a monotone increasing sequence of real numbers, that is,

$$b_1 \leq b_2 \leq b_3 \leq \cdots \leq b_n \leq b_{n+1} \leq \cdots.$$

It is an easy consequence of the l.u.b. property that if $\{b_n\}$ has an upper bound then $\lim\limits_{n \to \infty} b_n$ exists and is equal to $\text{l.u.b.}_n \, b_n$. This fact will be used in the proof of Lemma 1 below.

Proof of Theorem 19. The vertices of the polygons $r_m(P)$ which are all images of the same vertex of P will be called corresponding vertices. Let us denote a set of corresponding vertices of the polygons $r_m(P)$ by $\{v_m\}$. Thus, $r_1(v_1) = v_2, r_2(v_2) = v_3, \cdots$.

Lemma 1. As $m \to \infty$, v_m approaches a limit v; hence, the sequence $\{r_m(P)\}$ converges pointwise to $r(P)$, a k-gon ($k \leq n$).

To prove this lemma, we observe that if a_1, a_2, and a_3 are three non-collinear points interior to the convex hull H of P, then each sequence $\{\overline{a_j v_m}\}$ ($j = 1, 2, 3$) is a bounded monotone increasing sequence of posi-

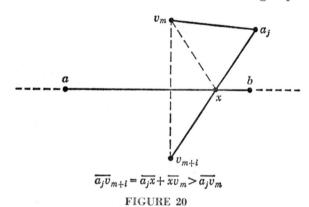

$$\overline{a_j v_{m+i}} = \overline{a_j x} + \overline{x v_m} > \overline{a_j v_m}$$

FIGURE 20

tive numbers (Fig. 20). Furthermore, $\overline{a_j v_m}$, the distance from a_j to v_m, is always bounded by one-half the perimeter of P. (Two points of a polygon can never be farther apart than one-half of its perimeter.) Therefore, by the least upper bound property of the real numbers, each sequence $\{\overline{a_j v_m}\}$ has a least upper bound R_j, which is also its limit. Thus, in the limit, the points v_m lie on each of three circles, the circles with centers a_j and radii R_j. But three circles whose centers are noncollinear intersect in at most one point. Therefore, the sequence $\{v_m\}$ converges to a limit v. This completes the proof of the lemma.

Note that, as far as we know at this point in the proof, $r(P)$ need not be convex and note further that some of its sides may conceivably lie in its interior as a result of squeezing which took place while the polygons $r_m(P)$ converged. See Figure 21 below.

Now let v be a vertex of the convex hull K of $r(P)$.

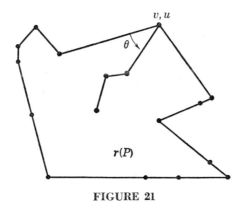

FIGURE 21

Lemma 2. The vertex v has moved only a finite number, N_v, of times.

To prove this we observe that the angle θ at a vertex v of $r(P)$ which is also a vertex of K is less than π (Fig. 21). The corresponding angles θ_m of the polygons $r_m(P)$ must converge to θ by Lemma 1. But if a vertex v_m with angle θ_m moves, then $\theta_{m+1} = 2\pi - \theta_m$. Since

$$\lim_{m \to \infty} \theta_m = \theta < \pi,$$

there exists a positive integer M such that if $m > M$, then $\theta_m < \pi$. Thus, $v_{M+1} = v_{M+2} = \cdots = v$. This proves the lemma.

Finally, let $N = \max N_v$ for v in K.

Lemma 3. $r_N(P) = K = r(P)$.

These equalities hold since, otherwise, a portion of $r_{N+1}(P)$ must lie outside the convex hull of $r_N(P)$, which, by Lemma 2, is K. This is clearly impossible. Lemma 3 implies the conclusion of the theorem. ∎

The above proof was constructed jointly by Professor R. H. Bing and the author. I thank him heartily for his enthusiastic coöperation.

Conjecture. If n is fixed, then N is bounded for all P and all choices of r_m's.

Can you prove or disprove this conjecture? Paul Erdös did.

PROBLEM

23. Prove that, given a convex n-gon with unequal sides, there exists a convex n-gon with n equal sides, with the same perimeter, but with a larger area.

The proposition that the regular n-gon has a greater area than a convex n-gon with equal sides and the same perimeter appears to be as difficult to prove as the Isoperimetric Theorem itself. Can you prove it using the fact that a bounded monotone increasing sequence of real numbers has a limit?

[3]

Inequalities and Calculus

6. The Number *e*

The number π is well known for its connection with circles. You may know that π is not a rational number. (Have you ever read a proof of this fact?) One can say even more about π than that it is an irrational number. The number π is not a root of any polynomial equation of the form

$$(1) \qquad \qquad \sum_0^n a_k x^k = 0,$$

where n is a positive integer, the coefficients a_k are all integers (positive, negative, or zero), and $a_n \neq 0$. Any number with this property is called a *transcendental* number. A number which is a root of some equation of the form (1) is called an *algebraic* number. Thus, we may classify the real numbers in two distinct ways: on the one hand, the class of real numbers is made up of rational and irrational numbers; and on the other hand, it is made up of algebraic and transcendental numbers. Algebraic numbers may be either rational or irrational. Transcendental numbers are always irrational. Can you prove that every rational number is algebraic?

Generally, it is extremely difficult to show that a particular number is transcendental. The fact that π is transcendental was not proved until the year 1882. C. L. F. Lindemann (1852–1939), a German mathematician, gave the first proof. Another transcendental number, which is of vital importance in calculus, is named *e*. The transcendency of *e* was proved by the French mathematician C. Hermite (1822–1905) in 1873. In this section we shall define the number *e* and become better acquainted with inequalities in the process.

We shall define *e* by means of two infinite sequences of positive numbers, $\{x_n\}$ and $\{y_n\}$, which have the following properties:

(1) $x_1 < x_2 < \cdots < x_n < x_{n+1} < \cdots$, that is, $\{x_n\}$ is a strictly increasing sequence;

(2) $y_1 > y_2 > \cdots > y_n > y_{n+1} > \cdots$, that is, $\{y_n\}$ is a strictly decreasing sequence;

(3) every number of the sequence $\{x_n\}$ is less than every number of the sequence $\{y_n\}$;

(4) to each positive integer N, there corresponds another positive integer M, $M = 4N$, such that

$$0 < y_n - x_n < \frac{1}{N} \quad \text{if} \quad n \geq M.$$

Definition 7. The number e is both the least upper bound of the sequence $\{x_n\}$ and the greatest lower bound of the sequence $\{y_n\}$ where

$$x_n = \left(1 + \frac{1}{n}\right)^n, \quad \text{and} \quad y_n = \left(1 + \frac{1}{n}\right)^{n+1} \quad (n = 1, 2, \cdots).$$

Approximate values of some of the numbers x_n and y_n are given in the table below and illustrated in Figure 22. (Some of the entries are exact.)

n	1	2	3	4	5	$\ldots$	50
x_n	2	2.25	2.37	2.44	2.49	$\ldots$	2.69
y_n	4	3.375	3.16	3.05	2.99	$\ldots$	2.74

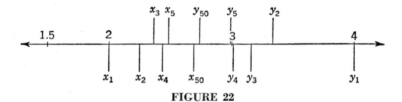

FIGURE 22

We shall now show that the sequences $\{x_n\}$ and $\{y_n\}$ defined above have the four properties promised. To establish the first two it is sufficient to show that for each positive integer n

$$x_n < x_{n+1} \quad \text{and} \quad y_n > y_{n+1}.$$

By the result of Problem 9 with $x = 1$ and $y = 1 + \frac{1}{n}$, we have

$$\sqrt[n+1]{1 \cdot \left(1 + \frac{1}{n}\right)^n} < \frac{1 + n\left(1 + \frac{1}{n}\right)}{n + 1} = 1 + \frac{1}{n + 1}.$$

Therefore by Theorem 6,

$$\left(1 + \frac{1}{n}\right)^n < \left(1 + \frac{1}{n + 1}\right)^{n+1}, \quad \text{or} \quad x_n < x_{n+1}.$$

It is easy to show in the same way that if

$$z_n = \left(1 - \frac{1}{n}\right)^n, \quad \text{then} \quad z_n < z_{n+1}.$$

We shall use this result to prove that $y_n > y_{n+1}$. Now,

$$y_n = \left(1 + \frac{1}{n}\right)^{n+1} = \left(\frac{n+1}{n}\right)^{n+1}$$

$$= \left(\frac{n}{n+1}\right)^{-(n+1)}$$

$$= \left(1 - \frac{1}{n+1}\right)^{-(n+1)};$$

that is,

$$y_n = z_{n+1}^{-1}.$$

Since $z_{n+1} > z_n$,

$$\frac{1}{z_{n+1}} < \frac{1}{z_n}.$$

Therefore,

$$y_n < y_{n-1} \quad (n = 2, 3, 4, \cdots)$$

or

$$y_{n+1} < y_n \quad (n = 1, 2, 3, \cdots).$$

This establishes the first and second properties of the sequences $\{x_n\}$ and $\{y_n\}$. It remains to verify the last two properties.

It is easy to see that $x_n < y_n$ for each n, since $y_n = (1 + 1/n)x_n$ and $1 + 1/n > 1$. We wish to prove that for any positive integers m and n, $x_n < y_m$. If $m = n$, we know this to be true. If $n > m$, then $n = m + k$ for some positive integer k; and by the second property,

$$x_n < y_n = y_{m+k} < y_m, \quad \text{or} \quad x_n < y_m.$$

You can show in almost the same way that if $n < m$, then $x_n < y_m$, and thus establish the third property.

Our last task is to prove that given any positive integer N, then whenever $n \geqq 4N$,

$$0 < y_n - x_n < \frac{1}{N}.$$

Now, for any positive n

$$y_n - x_n = \left(1 + \frac{1}{n}\right)x_n - x_n$$

$$= \frac{x_n}{n} > 0.$$

But for any positive n,

$$x_n < y_1 = 4,$$

by the third property. Therefore,

$$0 < y_n - x_n < \frac{4}{n} \quad (n = 1, 2, \cdots).$$

N is given; and for $n \geq 4N$, we observe that

$$\frac{4}{n} \leqq \frac{1}{N}.$$

Consequently,

$$0 < y_n - x_n < \frac{1}{N} \quad \text{if} \quad n \geq 4N.$$

This completes the proof of the fourth property.

Among other things, we have shown that $\{x_n\}$ has an upper bound and that $\{y_n\}$ has a lower bound. Therefore, by the least upper bound and greatest lower bound property of the reals cited above in §5, the l.u.b. $\underset{n}{x_n}$ and g.l.b. $\underset{n}{y_n}$ do exist. The fourth property of the sequences $\{x_n\}$ and $\{y_n\}$ makes it clear that Definition 7 is sound and self-consistent.

The sequences which we used to define e do not lend themselves to easy computation of the decimal expansion of e, as can be seen from the table above and the following numerical results. Let A_n, G_n, and H_n be the arithmetic, geometric, and harmonic means of x_n and y_n, respectively. [The harmonic mean H_n of x_n and y_n is defined to be

$$H_n = \frac{2x_n y_n}{x_n + y_n} = \left(\frac{x_n^{-1} + y_n^{-1}}{2}\right)^{-1}.$$

An easy computation shows that

$$x_n < H_n < y_n.]$$

Then we have:

n	1	2	3	4	$\ldots$	50
A_n	3	2.813	2.765	2.757	$\ldots$	2.7186
G_n	2.828	2.747	2.737	2.730	$\ldots$	2.7183
H_n	2.666	2.700	2.709	2.713	$\ldots$	2.7187

$$e = 2.7182 \cdots.$$

Moreover to obtain the entries in the above table easily, it is necessary to know $\log_{10} x_{50}$ to eight places! We note that each of the means A_n, G_n, and H_n converges to e very slowly and that for some time H_n is the best

$$\text{If} \quad n > m$$

$$m = n + k$$

$$\Lambda_m < y_m, \quad \Lambda_{n+k} \leq x_{n+k}$$

$$n < m \quad \text{then} \quad m = n + k$$

$$x_n < y_n \qquad\qquad y_{m+k} < y_m$$

$$y_m$$

$$\frac{N}{1} \gtreqless \frac{w}{h}$$

$$N \gtreqless \frac{h}{w}$$

$$Nh \gtreqless w$$

If $m < m'$, then $x_m < y_m$

$m' < m$ $m' = m + f$ $m - f = m$

$x_m < y_m = y_{m-f} < y_m$

$m' > m$

$m' = m + f$

$y_m < y_m = y_{m+f} < y_m$

approximation to e. This is interesting in view of the following result of Professor G. Pólya's: *The approximation that yields the minimum for the greatest possible absolute value of the relative error, committed in approximating an unknown quantity contained between two positive bounds, is the harmonic mean of these bounds.*

Proof. Let the unknown quantity x be bounded by a and b:

$$0 < a \leqq x \leqq b.$$

We wish to approximate x by p so that the maximum value of

$$\frac{|p - x|}{x} \quad \text{for} \quad a \leqq x \leqq b$$

is least. It is easy to see (Fig. 23) that the graph of $|p - x|/x$ is such that

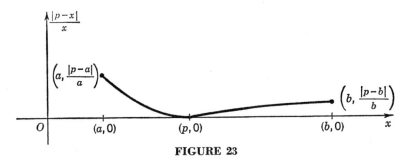

FIGURE 23

the maximum value of $f(x) = |p - x|/x$ is attained at $x = a$ or at $x = b$. Now if $0 < c < 1$ and $0 < \alpha < \beta$, then

$$\alpha < c\alpha + (1 - c)\beta < \beta.$$

[In fact, even if α and β are complex numbers, $c\alpha + (1 - c)\beta$ lies on the line segment joining α and β.] On the other hand,

$$\frac{a}{a + b} f(a) + \left(1 - \frac{a}{a + b}\right) f(b) = \frac{b - a}{b + a}.$$

Therefore, either

$$f(a) \leqq \frac{b - a}{b + a} \leqq f(b) \quad \text{or} \quad f(b) \leqq \frac{b - a}{b + a} \leqq f(a),$$

which means that

$$\max_{a \leqq x \leqq b} \frac{|p - x|}{x} \geqq \frac{b - a}{b + a}.$$

Equality holds if and only if $p = \dfrac{2ab}{a + b}$. ∎

The formula

$$e = \frac{1}{0!} + \frac{1}{1!} + \frac{1}{2!} + \frac{1}{3!} + \cdots = \sum_0^\infty \frac{1}{n!},$$

which we shall presently derive, gives accurate approximations to e, namely, $\sum_0^n 1/k!$ for small integers n. (Recall that $0! = 1$.) Using this series and time or using this series, time, and a computing machine, one can show that

$$e = 2.71828182845 \cdots.$$

Which method is more time consuming? (However, for large values of n, $n!$ is difficult to compute.)

In order to prove that $e = \sum_0^\infty 1/n!$, it is not necessary to use the calculus. All we need do is to prove the following theorem, which can be done by elementary means.

Theorem 20. If $n = 1, 2, 3, \cdots$, then

$$\left(1 + \frac{1}{n}\right)^n < \sum_0^n \frac{1}{k!} < \left(1 + \frac{1}{n}\right)^{n+1}.$$

Proof. It is easy to show that

$$\left(1 + \frac{1}{n}\right)^n < \sum_0^n \frac{1}{k!} \quad (n = 1, 2, \cdots).$$

We simply use the Binomial Theorem:

$$\left(1 + \frac{1}{n}\right)^n = 1 + \frac{n}{n} + \frac{n(n-1)}{1 \cdot 2} \cdot \frac{1}{n^2} + \frac{n(n-1)(n-2)}{3!} \cdot \frac{1}{n^3} + \cdots + \frac{1}{n^n}$$

and observe that

$$\frac{n(n-1)(n-2) \cdots (n-k)}{n^{k+1}} = \underbrace{\frac{n}{n} \cdot \frac{n-1}{n} \cdot \frac{n-2}{n} \cdots \cdots \frac{n-k}{n}}_{k+1 \text{ factors}} \leq 1$$

$(n = 1, 2, 3, \cdots)$.

Thus, the terms of the sum for $\left(1 + \frac{1}{n}\right)^n$ are each no greater than the corresponding terms of $\sum_0^n 1/k!$, and the desired result follows. On the other hand, the inequalities

$$\sum_0^n \frac{1}{k!} < \left(1 + \frac{1}{n}\right)^{n+1} \quad (n = 1, 2, 3, \cdots)$$

are not so easily established. We know that $(1 + 1/n)^{n+1}$ decreases as n increases. Hence, if we can show that for each positive integer n

$$\sum_0^n \frac{1}{k!} < \left(1 + \frac{1}{r}\right)^{r+1}$$

for some $r > n$, then the theorem is proved. We establish this inequality as follows.

Let n be given. Using the Binomial Theorem, we see that for any $r > n$,

$$\left(1 + \frac{1}{r}\right)^{r+1} - \sum_0^n \frac{1}{k!} = \left\{ (1^{r+1} - 1) + \left(\frac{r+1}{r} - 1\right) + \left[\frac{(r+1)r}{r^2} - 1\right]\frac{1}{2!} \right.$$

$$+ \left[\frac{(r+1)r(r-1)}{r^3} - 1\right]\frac{1}{3!} + \cdots$$

(2) $\qquad + \left[\frac{(r+1)r(r-1)\cdots(r-k+2)}{r^k} - 1\right]\frac{1}{k!}$

$$+ \cdots + \left.\left[\frac{(r+1)r(r-1)\cdots(r-n+2)}{r^n} - 1\right]\frac{1}{n!}\right\}$$

$$+ \frac{(r+1)r\cdots(r-n+1)}{r^{n+1}} \cdot \frac{1}{(n+1)!} + \cdots + \frac{1}{r^{r+1}}.$$

Let S be the sum of the n terms enclosed in the curly brackets above. We shall first prove that

$$|S| < \frac{1}{2(n+1)!}.$$

Simple arithmetic yields the identity

$$\frac{(r+1)r(r-1)\cdots[r-(k-2)]}{r^k} - 1 = \frac{a_1 r^{k-1} + a_2 r^{k-2} + \cdots + a_{k+1} r}{r^k}$$

$$(k = 1, 2, \cdots, n),$$

where the numbers a_i are integers which are independent of r. Let M_k be the largest of the a_i's. Then

$$\left|\frac{(r+1)r(r-1)\cdots[r-(k-2)]}{r^k} - 1\right| < \frac{M_k \sum_0^{k-2} r^i}{r^{k-1}} = \frac{M_k(r^{k-1} - 1)}{r^{k-1}(r-1)}$$

$$< \frac{M_k}{r-1}.$$

Since n is fixed, we have only a fixed number of M_k's, namely, n. Let M be the largest among them. Then

$$|S| < \frac{nM}{r-1}.$$

Therefore if $r > 1 + 2nM(n+1)! = N_1$,

$$|S| < \frac{1}{2(n+1)!}.$$

In a similar fashion one can show that the first term outside the curly brackets in (2) can be made larger than

$$\frac{3}{4} \cdot \frac{1}{(n+1)!}$$

by choosing r sufficiently large, say $r > N_2$. Consequently, for

$$r > N_1 + N_2,$$

$$\left(1 + \frac{1}{n}\right)^{n+1} - \sum_0^n \frac{1}{k!}$$

is positive. ∎

As we observed earlier, $n!$ is difficult to compute for large values of n. Fortunately, the tables can be turned, and e can be used to estimate $n!$.

PROBLEMS

24. Show that

$$\frac{(n+1)^{n+1}}{e^n} > n! > \left(\frac{n+1}{e}\right)^n \qquad (n = 1, 2, \cdots).$$

HINT: Use the fact that $\prod_1^n x_k < e^n$, $x_k = \left(1 + \frac{1}{n}\right)^n$.

This is but a crude estimate. A more precise one is given in §7.

25. Derive the inequalities

$$(n+1)^{\frac{1}{n+1}} < n^{1/n} \qquad (n = 3, 4, \cdots).$$

Why not $n = 1, 2, 3, \cdots$?

7. Examples from the Calculus

The Mean Value Theorem of differential calculus is:

If f is a real-valued continuous function defined on the closed interval $[a,b]$ and if f is differentiable everywhere in the interior of $[a,b]$, then

$$f(b) - f(a) = (b - a)f'(\xi),$$

where ξ is some number lying between a and b.

Thus, if upper and lower bounds for $f'(\xi)$ can be easily found, simple estimates of $f(b) - f(a)$ result. Let us consider some examples.

(a)　Let $f(x) = x^{1/3}$, $a = 23$ and $b = 27$. The function f is differentiable on $[a,b]$ and consequently satisfies the hypothesis of the Mean Value Theorem on $[a,b]$. Thus,

$$3 - 23^{1/3} = 4 \cdot \tfrac{1}{3} \cdot \xi^{-2/3} \quad (23 < \xi < 27).$$

Moreover,

$$\tfrac{1}{9} = (27)^{-2/3} < \xi^{-2/3} < [(\tfrac{8}{3})^3]^{-2/3} = \tfrac{9}{64}.$$

Therefore,

$$\tfrac{4}{27} < 3 - 23^{1/3} < \tfrac{3}{16},$$

or

$$2.81 < 23^{1/3} < 2.86.$$

Actually, $23^{1/3} = 2.8438 \cdots$.

(b)　The equation

$$x^3 + x^2 - 5x + k = 0 \quad (k \text{ real})$$

never has two roots on the interval $(0,1)$. For if it should have two such roots, say a and b, for some k, then by the Mean Value Theorem, which applies to the function $x^3 + x^2 - 5x + k$ on any interval whatsoever,

$$0 = 0 - 0 = f(b) - f(a) = (b - a) f'(\xi)$$
$$= (b - a)[3\xi^2 + 2\xi - 5]$$

$$(0 < a < \xi < b < 1).$$

But $3\xi^2 + 2\xi - 5$ is negative on $(0,1)$; hence, the assumption that f has two zeros on $(0,1)$ leads to a contradiction and is false.

(c)　The Arctan function is differentiable for all real x. Therefore, by the Mean Value Theorem, if $x > 1$,

$$\text{Arctan } x - \text{Arctan } 1 = (x - 1) \frac{1}{1 + \xi^2} \quad (1 < \xi < x).$$

In particular, since $(1 + \xi^2)^{-1}$ decreases as ξ increases from 1 to 9/8,

$$\frac{8}{145} = \frac{1}{8} \cdot \frac{64}{64 + 81} < \text{Arctan } 9/8 - \text{Arctan } 1 < \frac{1}{8} \cdot \frac{1}{1 + 1} = \frac{1}{16};$$

or

$$\text{Arctan } 1 + .0551 < \text{Arctan } 9/8 < \text{Arctan } 1 + .0625.$$

Since Arctan $1 = \pi/4 \approx .7854$, we find that

$$\text{Arctan } 9/8 = .844 \pm .004.$$

This estimate is rather good, considering the simple observations on which it is based. In general, however, the Mean Value Theorem is useful only when crude estimates suffice. On occasion it serves to give rough estimates of functions so complicated that more exact ones are exceedingly difficult to obtain.

    (d)   Let $f(x) = (a^2 + x)^{1/2}$. Clearly, f satisfies the Mean Value Theorem on $[0,b]$ if b is positive. Thus, if $b > 0$,

(3) $$f(b) = |a| + \frac{b}{2(a^2 + \xi)^{1/2}} \quad (0 < \xi < b).$$

It follows that for every x between 0 and b (including ξ)

$$(a^2 + x)^{1/2} < |a| + \frac{b}{2|a|}.$$

Consequently, replacing $(a^2 + \xi)^{1/2}$ by $|a| + b/2|a|$ in (3), we find that

$$f(b) > |a| + \frac{b}{2\left[|a| + \dfrac{b}{2|a|}\right]}.$$

Therefore, if a and b are positive, we have

$$a + \frac{ab}{2a^2 + b} < (a^2 + b)^{1/2} < a + \frac{b}{2a}.$$

For example,

$$3\tfrac{3}{10} < \sqrt{11} < 3\tfrac{1}{3} \quad (a = 3,\ b = 2).$$

    Suppose that f and g are continuous functions on the closed interval $[a,b]$. It is a fundamental property of the definite integral that if

$$f(x) \leqq g(x)$$

for all x on $[a,b]$, then

$$\int_a^b f(x)\, dx \leqq \int_a^b g(x)\, dx.$$

The inequality remains true, for example, if g is discontinuous at a or b, provided the limits $\lim_{x \to a^+} g(x)$ and $\lim_{x \to b^-} g(x)$ exist and are finite. Further, if $g(x) > f(x)$ at at least one point of continuity of f and g on $[a,b]$, then

$$\int_a^b f(x)\, dx < \int_a^b g(x)\, dx.$$

This simple theorem can be used to derive many interesting inequalities. The examples that follow are but a small sample.

(e) The inequality of Exercise 5, §1, may be derived as follows. We seek to estimate

$$\sum_{1}^{10^6} n^{-1/2}.$$

It is natural to choose (Fig. 24)

$$f(x) = x^{-1/2}, \quad \text{if } x > 1,$$

and

$$g(x) = n^{-1/2}, \quad \text{if } n \leq x < n+1 \quad (n = 1, 2, 3, \cdots).$$

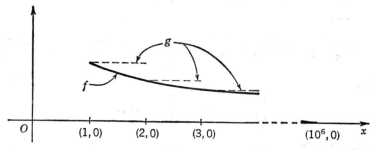

FIGURE 24

Then clearly,

$$n^{-1/2} = \int_{n}^{n+1} g(x)\, dx > \int_{n}^{n+1} x^{-1/2}\, dx = 2(\sqrt{n+1} - \sqrt{n}).$$

Hence,

$$\sum_{1}^{10^6} n^{-1/2} = \int_{1}^{10^6} g(x)\, dx > \int_{1}^{10^6} x^{-1/2}\, dx = 2(10^3 - 1) = 1998.$$

The inequality $1999 > \sum_{1}^{10^6} n^{-1/2}$ can be similarly demonstrated.

(f) Among the early triumphs of the calculus were the results of Leibnitz and Gregory that

$$\frac{\pi}{4} = \sum_{1}^{\infty} \frac{(-1)^{k+1}}{2k-1} \quad \text{and} \quad \ln 2 = \sum_{1}^{\infty} \frac{(-1)^{k+1}}{k}.$$

The most elementary and elegant derivations of these formulas are based on inequalities. Consider the function I, defined on the nonnegative integers, whose values are

$$I(n) = \int_{0}^{\pi/4} \tan^n \theta\, d\theta \quad (n = 0, 1, 2, \cdots).$$

A simple substitution and integration by parts reveal that for $n = 1, 2, \cdots$

$$I(2n) = \int_0^{\pi/4} \tan^{2n-2}\theta \,(\sec^2\theta - 1)\, d\theta,$$

$$= -I(2n-2) + \int_0^{\pi/4} \tan^{2n-2}\theta \sec^2\theta \, d\theta,$$

$$= -I(2n-2) + \frac{1}{2n-1},$$

$$= \frac{1}{2n-1} - \left[-I(2n-4) + \frac{1}{2n-3} \right]$$

$$\cdots$$

$$= \frac{1}{2n-1} - \frac{1}{2n-3} + \frac{1}{2n-5} - + \cdots + (-1)^{n-1}\cdot 1 + (-1)^n \frac{\pi}{4};$$

namely,

(4)
$$\left| \frac{\pi}{4} - \sum_1^n \frac{(-1)^{k+1}}{2k-1} \right| = I(2n).$$

Similarly, one can show that

(5)
$$\left| \tfrac{1}{2}\ln 2 - \sum_1^n \frac{(-1)^{k+1}}{2k} \right| = I(2n+1).$$

On the other hand, since $0 < \tan\theta < 1$ on $(0,\pi/4)$, $I(n)$ decreases as n increases; that is, I is a strictly decreasing function of n. Therefore, since

$$I(n) = -I(n-2) + \frac{1}{n-1},$$

or $\qquad\qquad\qquad\qquad\qquad\qquad\qquad\qquad\qquad (n = 2, 3, \cdots)$

$$I(n-2) + I(n) = \frac{1}{n-1},$$

we have the inequalities

$$I(n) < \frac{1}{2(n-1)} \quad \text{and} \quad I(n-2) > \frac{1}{2(n-1)}.$$

In short,

$$\frac{1}{2(n+1)} < I(n) < \frac{1}{2(n-1)}.$$

We obtain the following results by applying these inequalities to (4) and (5):

$$\frac{1}{2(2n+1)} < \left| \frac{\pi}{4} - \sum_1^n \frac{(-1)^{k+1}}{2k-1} \right| < \frac{1}{2(2n-1)},$$

and

$$\frac{1}{2(n+1)} < \left| \ln 2 - \sum_{1}^{n} \frac{(-1)^{k+1}}{k} \right| < \frac{1}{2n}.$$

Now we take the limit as $n \to \infty$ in the above inequalities, and in the limit we obtain the desired infinite series. Note that these inequalities provide sharper estimates of the differences between the sums of the infinite series and their partial sums than does the usual alternating series test estimate of "less than the absolute value of the first neglected term." The inequalities also exhibit the fact that the series converge so slowly as to be poor tools for computing either π or $\ln 2$.

(g) The product which we studied in §1 was more carefully estimated by the British mathematician John Wallis (1616–1703) three hundred years ago. He showed that

$$\textbf{(6)} \qquad \frac{1}{\sqrt{\pi(n + \frac{1}{2})}} < \frac{1 \cdot 3 \cdots (2n-1)}{2 \cdot 4 \cdots 2n} < \frac{1}{\sqrt{\pi n}} \qquad (n = 1, 2, \cdots).$$

In order to derive Wallis's result, one considers the real-valued function J defined on the nonnegative integers, whose values are

$$J(n) = \int_{0}^{\pi/2} \sin^n \theta \, d\theta \quad (n = 0, 1, 2, \cdots).$$

In analogy with the last example, we can obtain a formula connecting $J(n+2)$ and $J(n)$: a simple substitution and integration by parts show that

$$J(n+2) = \int_{0}^{\pi/2} \sin^n \theta \, (1 - \cos^2 \theta) \, d\theta$$

$$= J(n) - \int_{0}^{\pi/2} \cos \theta \, \frac{d\,[\sin^{n+1} \theta / (n+1)]}{d\theta} \, d\theta$$

$$= J(n) - \left\{ \left[\frac{\sin^{n+1} \theta \cos \theta}{n+1} \right]_{0}^{\pi/2} + \int_{0}^{\pi/2} \frac{\sin^{n+1} \theta \sin \theta}{n+1} \, d\theta \right\}$$

$$= J(n) - \frac{1}{n+1} J(n+2).$$

Thus,

$$J(n+2) = \frac{n+1}{n+2} J(n).$$

It follows by repeated application of this formula that

$$J(2n) = \frac{2n-1}{2n} \cdot \frac{2n-3}{2n-2} \cdots \frac{3}{2} \cdot J(0)$$

$$= \frac{2n-1}{2n} \cdot \frac{2n-3}{2n-2} \cdots \frac{3}{2} \cdot \frac{\pi}{2};$$

and

$$J(2n+1) = \frac{2n}{2n+1} \cdot \frac{2n-2}{2n-1} \cdots \frac{2}{3} \cdot J(1);$$

$$= \frac{2n}{2n+1} \cdot \frac{2n-2}{2n-1} \cdots \frac{2}{3} \cdot 1.$$

Therefore,

$$J(2n+1)J(2n) = \frac{1}{2n+1} \cdot \frac{\pi}{2} \quad (n = 1, 2, \cdots).$$

But

$$J(2n) > J(2n+1) \quad \text{and} \quad J(2n-1) > J(2n),$$

since

$$0 < \sin\theta < 1 \quad \text{for} \quad 0 < \theta < \frac{\pi}{2}.$$

Consequently,

$$J^2(2n) > \frac{1}{2n+1} \cdot \frac{\pi}{2} \quad \text{and} \quad J^2(2n) < \frac{1}{2n} \cdot \frac{\pi}{2},$$

or

$$\frac{\pi}{2(2n+1)} < \left(\frac{2n-1}{2n} \cdot \frac{2n-3}{2n-2} \cdots \frac{3}{4} \cdot \frac{1}{2}\right)^2 \frac{\pi^2}{4} < \frac{\pi}{4n} \quad (n = 1, 2, \cdots).$$

This inequality is equivalent to (6). Incidentally, John Wallis invented (in 1655) the symbol "∞" for "infinity."

8.   Approximation by Polynomials

Taylor's Theorem, published by the English mathematician B. Taylor (1685–1731) in 1715, is a generalization of the Mean Value Theorem. In some contexts it is even more useful. The Mean Value Theorem gives an approximation to a differentiable function f in a neighborhood of a point a.

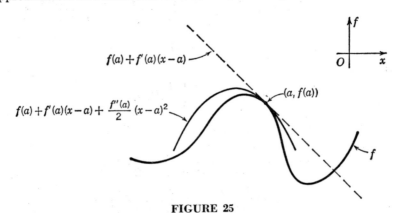

FIGURE 25

The approximation is $f(a)$. It is natural to attempt to improve this approximation by using (Fig. 25) an nth degree polynomial $P_n(x)$ in $(x - a)$ which satisfies the conditions

$$P_n^{(k)}(a) = f^{(k)}(a) \quad (k = 0, 1, \cdots, n).$$

These conditions imply that

$$P_n(x) = \sum_0^n \frac{f^{(k)}(a)}{k!} (x - a)^k.$$

Lagrange's version of Taylor's Theorem is:

Theorem. If f and its first $n + 1$ derivatives are continuous on an open interval (c,d), and if x and a are points of (c,d), then

$$f(x) = P_n(x) + \frac{f^{(n+1)}(\theta_{n+1})}{(n + 1)!} (x - a)^{n+1}$$

where θ_{n+1} is some number between a and x.

A particularly simple proof of this theorem, which is perhaps less mysterious than some others, is based upon some elementary inequalities.

Proof. The theorem is obviously true if $x = a$. Throughout the proof we shall therefore assume $x \neq a$. Let the function $R = f - P_n$. We seek to demonstrate that there is a number θ_{n+1}, lying somewhere between a and x, such that

$$R(x) = \frac{f^{(n+1)}(\theta_{n+1})}{(n + 1)!} (x - a)^{n+1}.$$

Since f has $n + 1$ continuous derivatives on (c,d) and since P_n has infinitely many, R is $n + 1$ times continuously differentiable on (c,d). Further,

(7) $$R^{(k)}(a) = 0 \quad (k = 0, 1, \cdots, n),$$

and

$$R^{(n)}(x) = f^{(n)}(x) - P_n^{(n)}(x) \quad (x \text{ on } (c,d)).$$

But $P_n^{(n)}(x)$ is constant ($P_n(x)$ is an nth-degree polynomial), and $P_n^{(n)}(a) = f^{(n)}(a)$. Therefore, $P_n^{(n)}(x) \equiv f^{(n)}(a)$, and

$$R^{(n)}(x) = f^{(n)}(x) - f^{(n)}(a).$$

Let us now suppose for the sake of argument that $x > a$. The function $f^{(n)}(x)$ satisfies the hypothesis of the Mean Value Theorem on $[a,x]$. It follows that

$$f^{(n)}(x) - f^{(n)}(a) = f^{(n+1)}(\theta_1)(x - a),$$

where θ_1 lies somewhere between x and a. Therefore,

$$(8) \qquad R^{(n)}(x) = f^{(n+1)}(\theta_1)(x-a).$$

Since $f^{(n+1)}$ is by hypothesis continuous on (c,d), it is bounded on the closed interval $[a,x]$. Let m and M be the maximum and minimum values of $f^{(n+1)}$, respectively, on $[a,x]$. Then by (8),

$$m(t-a) \leq R^{(n)}(t) \leq M(t-a) \quad (t \text{ on } [a,x]).$$

Moreover, inequality must hold for at least one t unless $M = m$. Consequently,

$$m\int_a^x (t-a)\,dt < \int_a^x R^{(n)}(t)\,dt < M\int_a^x (t-a)\,dt,$$

or by (7),

$$\tfrac{1}{2}m(x-a)^2 < R^{(n-1)}(x) < \tfrac{1}{2}M(x-a)^2.$$

Since $f^{(n+1)}$ is continuous on $[a,x]$, there must be some number θ_2 on (a,x) such that

$$f^{(n+1)}(\theta_2) = \frac{2R^{(n-1)}(x)}{(x-a)^2} \quad (\text{recall that } x \neq a).$$

Thus,

$$(9) \qquad R^{(n-1)}(x) = \tfrac{1}{2}f^{(n+1)}(\theta_2)(x-a)^2.$$

Repeating the above argument while using (9) instead of (8), we can show that

$$R^{(n-2)}(x) = \frac{1}{2\cdot 3}f^{(n+1)}(\theta_3)(x-a)^3,$$

where θ_3 lies between a and x. After a total of n steps of this kind we reach the conclusion:

$$R(x) = \frac{1}{(n+1)!}f^{(n+1)}(\theta_{n+1})(x-a)^{n+1}$$

for some number θ_{n+1} between a and x. An analogous result holds if $x < a$. ∎

As an example of the use of Taylor's formula, we estimate the integral

$$I = \int_1^2 x^{1/2}\sin x\,dx.$$

The sine function fulfills the hypothesis of Taylor's Theorem on any interval. We apply the theorem to $\sin x$ with $a = 0$, and we find that

$$\sin x = x - \frac{x^3}{3!} + \frac{\sin\theta}{4!}x^4 \quad (0 < \theta < x).$$

Thus,

$$x - \frac{x^3}{3!} < \sin x \leq x - \frac{x^3}{3!} + \frac{x^4}{4!}$$

if $2 \geq x \geq 1$. Therefore,

$$\int_1^2 x^{1/2} \left(x - \frac{x^3}{3!} \right) dx < I \leq \int_1^2 x^{1/2} \left(x - \frac{x^3}{3!} + \frac{x^4}{4!} \right) dx,$$

or

$$\frac{2^3 \cdot 17\sqrt{2} - 49}{3^3 \cdot 5} < I \leq \frac{2^3 \cdot 17\sqrt{2} - 49}{3^3 \cdot 5} + \frac{2}{11 \cdot 4!} (2^{11/2} - 1).$$

Since $2(2^{11/2} - 1)/(4! \cdot 11)$ is about $\frac{3}{10}$, this estimate is not very sharp. On the other hand, with time (and that perhaps means money) and a computing machine one could compute the value of I with an error less than 10^{-4} by using Taylor's formula with a large enough n.   For the purposes of such a computation it would be better to expand $\sin x$ in powers of $(x - \pi/2)$, and it would be still better to approximate the integrand by different functions on each of several subintervals of $[1,2]$.

We next consider a second application of Taylor's Theorem.   The integral

$$K(k) = \int_0^{\pi/2} \frac{d\theta}{\sqrt{1 - k^2 \sin^2 \theta}}$$

is called the complete elliptic integral of the first kind.   Let us compute $K(\frac{1}{4})$ correctly to four decimal places.   Consider the function f, defined for $x < 1$ by $f(x) = (1 - x)^{-1/2}$.   If $0 < x < \frac{1}{16}$ ($\frac{1}{16} \geq k^2 \sin^2 \theta \geq 0$), then Taylor's Theorem guarantees that

$$f(x) = 1 + \tfrac{1}{2}x + \tfrac{3}{8}x^2 + R(x),$$

where

$$R(x) = 5 \cdot 2^{-4}x^3 (1 - \theta)^{-9/2} \quad (0 < \theta < \tfrac{1}{16}).$$

Thus,

$$\left| K(\tfrac{1}{4}) - \int_0^{\pi/2} \left(1 + \frac{1}{2} \cdot \frac{\sin^2 \theta}{16} + \frac{3}{8} \cdot \frac{\sin^4 \theta}{256} \right) d\theta \right|$$

$$< \frac{5}{2^4 (16)^3} \left(\frac{15}{16} \right)^{-9/2} \int_0^{\pi/2} \sin^6 \theta \, d\theta$$

$$= \frac{\pi}{36(15)^{5/2}}$$

$$< 10^{-4},$$

since

$$\int_0^{\pi/2} \sin^{2n} \theta \, d\theta = \frac{1 \cdot 3 \cdots (2n - 1)}{2 \cdot 4 \cdots 2n} \cdot \frac{\pi}{2} \quad (n = 1, 2, \cdots).$$

An estimate of $K(\frac{1}{4})$ correct with an error less than 10^{-4} is therefore

$$\frac{\pi}{2}\left[1 + \frac{1}{32}\cdot\frac{1}{2} + \frac{3}{2^{11}}\cdot\frac{1\cdot 3}{2\cdot 4}\right] \quad \text{or} \quad 1.5962\cdots .$$

Approximations to definite integrals may often be obtained much more simply. For example, if $k > 2$, then

$$\frac{1}{2} = \int_0^1 x\,dx > \int_0^1 \frac{x\,dx}{(1+x^k)^{1/3}} > \int_0^1 \frac{x\,dx}{(1+x^2)^{1/3}} = \tfrac{3}{4}[2^{2/3} - 1] > .44.$$

Taylor's Theorem guarantees that, subject to rather stringent conditions, a function can be approximated by a particular class of polynomials, namely, those of the form $\sum_0^n f^{(k)}(a)(x-a)^k/k!$. Let us call them the Taylor polynomials of f at a. If the graph of f is not smooth in the neighborhood of the point $(a, f(a))$, as in Figure 26, then near a the derivatives of

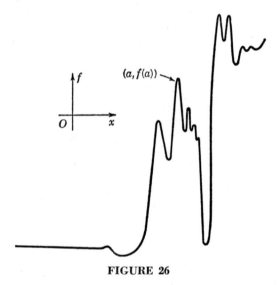

FIGURE 26

f may be very large in comparison with $f(a)$, even if they exist; hence, the Taylor polynomials of f at a may be poor approximations to f outside of a very small neighborhood of a. Weierstrass discovered a theorem which gives one hope that other more useful types of polynomial approximations to continuous functions can be determined.

Theorem. (*Weierstrass Approximation Theorem*). If f is continuous on $[a,b]$, then to each positive number ϵ there corresponds a positive integer n and a polynomial P_n of degree n such that

$$\left|f(x) - P_n(x)\right| < \epsilon \quad \text{if } a \leq x \leq b.$$

The polynomial P_n and n are, of course, not unique. Thus, polynomial approximations to any continuous function exist which have a predetermined accuracy on an entire interval of fixed length. Naturally, they may be hard to find; not all things that exist can be constructed. Nevertheless, we shall prove this theorem by exhibiting a sequence of polynomials $\{B_n(x)\}$, depending on f, which converge uniformly to f on $[a,b]$; namely, we shall show that, given $\epsilon > 0$, there exists a positive integer N such that

$$\left|f(x) - B_n(x)\right| < \epsilon$$

for all x on $[a,b]$ and *all* integers $n > N$. The discovery of the polynomials B_n and their remarkable property is due to the venerable Russian mathematician S. N. Bernšteĭn (1880—).

Definition 8. The polynomial

$$B_n(x) \equiv \sum_0^n f\left(\frac{k}{n}\right)\binom{n}{k} x^k(1-x)^{n-k}, \quad \binom{n}{k} = \frac{n!}{k!(n-k)!},$$

is the Bernšteĭn polynomial of degree n corresponding to a real-valued function f defined on $[0,1]$.

Theorem 21 (*Bernšteĭn*). If f is continuous on $[0,1]$, its Bernšteĭn polynomials B_n converge uniformly to it on $[0,1]$ as $n \to \infty$.

The question immediately arises: how did Bernšteĭn ever think of approximating a function by such polynomials? Conceivably, the answer is that he knew the theory of probability well enough to think of applying it to approximation theory. Suppose one has a coin with the property that the probability of its showing heads after a single toss is $x(0 \leq x \leq 1)$. The probability of its showing tails after one toss is then $1 - x$. Moreover, the probability of exactly k heads in n tosses is $\binom{n}{k}x^k(1-x)^{n-k}$. Thus it must be that

$$\sum_0^n \binom{n}{k} x^k(1-x)^{n-k} \equiv 1 \equiv \sum_0^n \text{(probability of exactly } k \text{ heads in } n \text{ tosses of the coin)},$$

since some number of heads from 0 to n must have appeared in n tosses of the coin. And indeed,

$$1 \equiv [(1-x) + x]^n \equiv \sum_0^n x^k(1-x)^{n-k}.$$

A Bernšteĭn polynomial of degree n associated with a function f may be assigned the following interpretation. Given a positive integer n, consider the set of numbers $\{f(k/n)\}$, $k = 0, 1, \cdots, n$. If n is large and x lies somewhere in [0,1], then one or more of the numbers $f(k/n)$ lie close to $f(x)$. The question is: If x is some number in [0,1] to be chosen at random in the future and if f is some function continuous on [0,1], also to be chosen at random in the future, which weighted sum

$$\sum_{k=0}^{k=n} c(k,x) f\left(\frac{k}{n}\right) \quad \left(\sum_0^n c(k,x) = 1\right),$$

of the numbers $f(k/n)$ should one prescribe so as to be sure of a good approximation to $f(x)$ when x and f are chosen? The answer clearly depends on what is meant by a "good approximation." If this is to mean that

$$\max \left| f(x) - \sum_0^n c(k,x) f\left(\frac{k}{n}\right) \right|$$

is small, then Bernsteĭn's choice of the weights $c(k,x)$ is a good one. He chose the $c(k,x)$'s to be the probabilities $\binom{n}{k} x^k (1-x)^{n-k}$. It is a simple consequence of a theorem called the *Law of Large Numbers*, in the theory of probability, that the weighted sums $B_n(x)$ corresponding to this choice of $c(k,x)$ converge uniformly to f on [0,1] as $n \rightarrow \infty$. [Suppose in a certain population c_k men have exactly f_k wives. Then the total number of wives is $\sum f_k c_k$; and one would expect that if one chose a man at random, he would have

$$\frac{\sum f_k c_k}{\sum c_k}$$

wives, namely, the average number of wives per man. Moreover, the larger the population the greater would be one's expectation that a man chosen at random would be an average man. Now suppose that an outcome of exactly k heads in n tosses of the aforementioned coin is rewarded with $f(k/n)$ dollars. The expected number of dollars after n tosses would be, in analogy with the expected number of wives in the last example,

$$\frac{\sum_0^n f\left(\frac{k}{n}\right)\binom{n}{k} x^k (1-x)^{n-k}}{\sum_0^n \binom{n}{k} x^k (1-x)^{n-k}},$$

which is simply $B_n(x)$. For a careful, detailed exposition of probability theory, I suggest that you read *An Introduction to Probability Theory and Its Applications*, Vol. 1, by W. Feller (John Wiley and Sons, New York, 1950).] Thus, once Bernšteĭn thought of the probabilities $\binom{n}{k} x^k (1-x)^{n-k}$, he knew Theorem 21. After his discovery, he was able to prove Theorem 21 without using the Law of Large Numbers.

We complete our discussion of Bernšteĭn polynomials with Bernšteĭn's proofs of Theorem 21 and the Weierstrass Approximation Theorem. His proof of Theorem 21, although it is elegant, simple, and clear, is demanding. I urge you to accept the task of mastering it as a challenge. If you take up the challenge and master the proof, you will have won a great prize. Those interested in still greater rewards should read N. I. Ahiezer's superb book, *Theory of Approximation*, translation by C. J. Hyman (F. Ungar Publ. Co., New York, 1956). (NOTE: The mathematical English of the translation is often awkward; the original Russian version reads much more smoothly. The translation of the original Russian title is *Lectures on the Theory of Approximation*.)

Lemma.

$$0 \leq \sum_{k=0}^{n} \left(\frac{k}{n} - x\right)^2 \binom{n}{k} x^k (1-x)^{n-k} \leq \frac{1}{4n}$$

for $0 \leq x \leq 1$.

Proof. For brevity, we write

$$g_k = \binom{n}{k} x^k (1-x)^{n-k}.$$

If we can evaluate the sums $\sum_0^n k^2 g_k / n^2$, $\sum_0^n xk g_k / n$ and $\sum_0^n x^2 g_k$ in short, simple form, then we can perhaps estimate the sum involved in the statement of the lemma. We already know that

(10)
$$\sum_0^n x^2 g_k = x^2.$$

Now consider the identity

(11)
$$(u+v)^n = \sum_0^n \binom{n}{k} u^k v^{n-k},$$

which reduces to $1 = \sum_0^n g_k$ when $u = x$ and $v = 1-x$. If we assume u to be a variable and if we differentiate both sides of (11) with respect to u, we obtain the identity

$$n(u+v)^{n-1} = \sum_0^n k \binom{n}{k} u^{k-1} v^{n-k},$$

or

(12)
$$nu(u+v)^{n-1} = \sum_0^n k \binom{n}{k} u^k v^{n-k}.$$

Thus upon choosing $u = x$ and $v = 1 - x$, we find that

$$\sum_0^n k g_k = nx,$$

or

(13)
$$\sum_0^n x \frac{k}{n} g_k = x^2.$$

What was successful once may be successful twice; hence, we next differentiate both sides of (12) with respect to u. The result is

$$n(u + v)^{n-1} + n(n - 1)u(u + v)^{n-2} = \sum_0^n k^2 \binom{n}{k} u^{k-1} v^{n-1}.$$

If we multiply both members of this identity by u/n^2 and again set $u = x$ and $v = 1 - x$, we find that

(14)
$$\sum_0^n \frac{k^2}{n^2} g_k = \frac{x}{n} + \left(1 - \frac{1}{n}\right) x^2.$$

It now follows from the identities (10), (13), and (14) that

$$\sum_0^n \left(\frac{k}{n} - x\right)^2 g_k = x^2 - 2x^2 + \frac{x}{n} + \left(1 - \frac{1}{n}\right) x^2$$

$$= \frac{-(x^2 - x)}{n}$$

$$= \frac{-(x - \frac{1}{2})^2 + \frac{1}{4}}{n}.$$

Therefore,

$$0 \leq \sum_0^n \left(\frac{k}{n} - x\right)^2 g_k \leq \frac{1}{4n} \quad \text{if} \quad 0 \leq x \leq 1.$$

Equality holds if and only if $x = \frac{1}{2}$. ∎

Besides this lemma, we need in the proof a fundamental property of continuous functions, which may be new to you. This is *uniform continuity*.

Definition 9. A function f, defined on an interval $[a,b]$, is uniformly continuous on $[a,b]$ if to any positive number p (no matter how small), there corresponds a positive number d such that the hypothesis

$$x_1 \text{ and } x_2 \text{ lie on } [a,b] \quad \text{and} \quad |x_1 - x_2| < d$$

implies the conclusion

$$|f(x_1) - f(x_2)| < p.$$

The result we require is

Theorem. If a function is continuous on the closed interval $[a,b]$, then it is uniformly continuous on that interval.

The reader who is interested in its proof will find it in any good book on advanced calculus. It is easy to prove, however, that *every function having a continuous derivative on a closed interval $[a,b]$ is uniformly continuous there.*

Proof. Let p be given. Since f' is continuous on $[a,b]$, f satisfies the hypothesis of the Mean Value Theorem there. It follows that if x_1 and x_2 are any two points of $[a,b]$,

$$|f(x_1) - f(x_2)| = |f'(\theta)| \cdot |x_2 - x_1|,$$

for some θ lying between x_1 and x_2. The hypothesis that f' is continuous on $[a,b]$ also implies that f' is bounded there, say by M. Therefore, whenever $|x_1 - x_2| < p/M = d$, $|f(x_1) - f(x_2)| < p$. ∎

Proof of Theorem 21. We are given an $\epsilon > 0$. We seek to demonstrate the existence of an integer N such that if $n > N$, then $|f(x) - B_n(x)| < \epsilon$ for all x on $[0,1]$. We begin by asserting the existence of two other numbers. First, since f is continuous on $[0,1]$, so is $|f|$; and therefore $|f|$ has a maximum, M, on $[0,1]$. Second, f is uniformly continuous on $[0,1]$, and consequently we know that to the number $\epsilon/2$ there corresponds a number $\delta > 0$ such that

$$(15) \qquad |f(x_1) - f(x_2)| < \frac{\epsilon}{2}$$

whenever $|x_1 - x_2| < \delta$ and x_1 and x_2 are points of $[0,1]$. We also know

$$f(x) = f(x) \cdot 1 = f(x) \cdot \sum_0^n g_k = \sum_0^n f(x)g_k.$$

Thus,

$$|f(x) - B_n(x)| = \left| \sum_0^n \left[f(x) - f\left(\frac{k}{n}\right) \right] g_k \right|;$$

and it follows from the triangle inequality (see §2) that

$$(16) \quad |f(x) - B_n(x)| \leq \sum_0^n \left| f(x) - f\left(\frac{k}{n}\right) \right| g_k \quad \text{(note that } g_k \geq 0 \text{ on } [0,1]).$$

Our problem is to show that the sum on the right is less than ϵ if n is chosen large enough. Imagine that an x on $[0,1]$ is given. Surely the terms corresponding to those values of k such that k/n is close to x are small. It turns out that with the help of the lemma we can prove that the remaining terms are also small, provided n is large enough. We proceed by dividing the n allowed integers k into two classes, A and B:

$$k \text{ is in } A \quad \text{if} \quad \left| x - \frac{k}{n} \right| < \delta;$$

$$k \text{ is in } B \quad \text{if} \quad \left| x - \frac{k}{n} \right| \geq \delta.$$

The classes A and B depend upon x and n. Nevertheless, we can obtain an upper bound for the right-hand member of **(16)** which is independent of x and n, provided n is sufficiently large.

Suppose k is in A. Then by **(15)**,

$$\left| f(x) - f\left(\frac{k}{n}\right) \right| < \frac{\epsilon}{2}.$$

Therefore,

$$(17) \qquad \sum_{k \text{ in } A} \left| f(x) - f\left(\frac{k}{n}\right) \right| g_k < \frac{\epsilon}{2} \sum_{k \text{ in } A} g_k \leq \frac{\epsilon}{2} \sum_{0}^{n} g_k = \frac{\epsilon}{2} \cdot 1.$$

On the other hand, if k lies in B, then

$$\frac{\left| \dfrac{k}{n} - x \right|^2}{\delta^2} \geq 1$$

so that

$$\sum_{k \text{ in } B} \left| f(x) - f\left(\frac{k}{n}\right) \right| g_k \leq \sum_{k \text{ in } B} \left| f(x) - f\left(\frac{k}{n}\right) \right| \frac{\left(\dfrac{k}{n} - x \right)^2}{\delta^2} g_k.$$

But

$$\left| f(x) - f\left(\frac{k}{n}\right) \right| \leq |f(x)| + \left| f\left(\frac{k}{n}\right) \right| \leq M + M = 2M.$$

Therefore,

$$\sum_{k \text{ in } B} \left| f(x) - f\left(\frac{k}{n}\right) \right| g_k \leq \frac{2M}{\delta^2} \sum_{k \text{ in } B} \left(\frac{k}{n} - x \right)^2 g_k \leq \frac{2M}{\delta^2} \sum_{0}^{n} \left(\frac{k}{n} - x \right)^2 g_k.$$

We now apply the lemma and conclude that

$$\sum_{k \text{ in } B} \left| f(x) - f\left(\frac{k}{n}\right) \right| g_k \leq \frac{M}{n\delta^2}.$$

But δ depends only on ϵ and f, and M depends only on f. Consequently, there is a smallest integer, call it N, satisfying the inequality

$$\frac{M}{n\delta^2} < \frac{\epsilon}{2}.$$

Hence,

(18) $$\sum_{k \text{ in } B} \left| f(x) - f\left(\frac{k}{n}\right) \right| g_k < \frac{\epsilon}{2} \quad \text{if} \quad n \geq N.$$

We now complete the proof. It follows from (17) and (18) that

$$\sum_{0}^{n} \left| f(x) - f\left(\frac{k}{n}\right) \right| g_k = \sum_{k \text{ in } A} \left| f(x) - f\left(\frac{k}{n}\right) \right| g_k + \sum_{k \text{ in } B} \left| f(x) - f\left(\frac{k}{n}\right) \right| g_k$$

$$< \frac{\epsilon}{2} + \frac{\epsilon}{2} = \epsilon,$$

provided $n \geq N$. Using this result and (16), we obtain the desired final conclusion. ∎

It remains to prove the Weierstrass Approximation Theorem.

Proof. A function f, continuous on an interval $[a,b]$, is given. Now as t varies from 0 to 1, $a + t(b - a)$ varies from a to b (Fig. 27); and conversely, as $a + t(b - a)$ varies from a to b, t varies from 0 to 1. Let

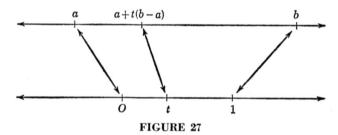

FIGURE 27

$F(t) = f(a + t(b - a))$. Then F is continuous on $[0,1]$; and given $\epsilon > 0$, there is an N such that

$$|F(t) - B_n(t,F)| < \epsilon \quad \text{if} \quad n > N.$$

$[B_n(t,F)$ is written for $B_n(t)$ in order to emphasize the fact that B_n depends upon F.] But

$$t = \frac{x - a}{b - a} \quad \text{and} \quad F\left(\frac{x - a}{b - a}\right) \equiv f(x).$$

Therefore,

$$\left| f(x) - B_n\left(\frac{x - a}{b - a}, F\right) \right| < \epsilon \quad \text{if} \quad n > N.$$

Moreover, $B_n\left(\dfrac{x - a}{b - a}, F\right)$ is a polynomial of degree n in x, since $(x - a) \cdot (b - a)$ is linear in x; and $B_n(t,F)$ is a polynomial of degree n in t. ∎

PROBLEMS

26. (a) Show that

$$\frac{9}{8} < \sum_1^{100} \frac{1}{n^3} < \frac{3}{2}.$$

Can you improve these estimates?

(b) Find upper and lower bounds for $\sum_1^{100} \ln n$.

27. (a) Prove that if $x > -1$,

$$\ln (1 + x) \equiv \int_0^x \frac{dt}{1+t} = \sum_1^n (-1)^{k-1} \frac{x^k}{k} + (-1)^n \int_0^x \frac{t^n}{1+t}\, dt.$$

(b) Next estimate the integral $\int_0^x t^n (1 + t)^{-1}\, dt$ and show that if $|x| \leq \frac{1}{2}$,

$$\left| (-1)^n \int_0^x t^n (1 + t)^{-1}\, dt \right| \leq 2 \left| \int_0^x t^n\, dt \right| \leq 2^{-n}(n + 1)^{-1}.$$

(c) Using the above results, obtain the conclusion

$$\ln (1 + x) - \ln (1 - x) = 2 \sum_0^n \frac{x^{2k+1}}{2k + 1} + R_n$$

where

$$|R_n| \leq 2^{-2n-1}(1 + n)^{-1} \quad \text{if} \quad |x| \leq \frac{1}{2}.$$

For example, if $x = -\frac{1}{3}$, $\ln \dfrac{1 + x}{1 - x} = -\ln 2$; and therefore,

$$\left| \ln 2 - 2 \left(\frac{1}{3} + \frac{1}{3^4} + \frac{1}{3^5 \cdot 5} + \frac{1}{3^7 \cdot 7} \right) \right| < 2^{-9}.$$

Improve this estimate by taking advantage of the fact that $\left| -\frac{1}{3} \right| < \frac{1}{2}$.

28. Establish the following inequalities:

(a) $\dfrac{1}{2} < \displaystyle\int_0^{1/2} \dfrac{dx}{\sqrt{1 - x^4}} < \dfrac{\pi}{6}.$

(b) $\dfrac{1}{2} < \displaystyle\int_0^1 \dfrac{dx}{\sqrt{4 - x^2 + x^4}} < \dfrac{\pi}{6}.$

(c) $\dfrac{1}{28} < \displaystyle\int_0^1 \dfrac{x^{20}}{(1 + x^{11})^{1/3}} < \dfrac{1}{21}.$

(d) $0 < \displaystyle\int_0^{1/2} \sin x \ln (1 + x)\, dx < \dfrac{7}{96}.$

29. Since

$$(1 + 2x)^{1/2} = 1 + x - \frac{x^2}{2} + \frac{x^3}{3} - \frac{x^4}{8} (1 + 2\theta x)^{-7/2} \quad (0 < \theta < 1)$$

and since

$$1 + x - \frac{1}{2} \cdot \frac{x^2}{1 + x} = 1 + x - \frac{x^2}{2} + \frac{x^3}{3} - \frac{1}{2} \cdot \frac{x^4}{1 + x},$$

$$(1 + 2x)^{1/2} - \left[1 + x - \frac{1}{2} \frac{x^2}{1 + x} \right] = \frac{1}{8x^4} \left(\frac{4}{1 + x} - \frac{x^4}{(1 + 2\theta x)^{7/2}} \right).$$

Prove that

$$\left| (u^2 + v)^{1/2} - \left(|u| + \frac{v}{2|u|} - \frac{v^2}{4|u|\,(2u^2 + v)} \right) \right| < \frac{v^4}{32|u|^7}$$

if $0 < v/u^2 < v$.
For example,

$$\left| \sqrt{11} - \left(3 + \frac{1}{3} - \frac{4}{4\cdot 3\,(18 + 2)} \right) \right| < \frac{2^4}{32\cdot 3^7},$$

or

$$|\sqrt{11} - 3.31666\cdots| < 2.3\cdot 10^{-4}.$$

30. The most often used estimate of $n!$ is Stirling's:

$$(2\pi n)^{1/2} \left(\frac{n}{e} \right)^n < n! < (2\pi n)^{1/2} \left(\frac{n}{e} \right)^n e^{1/12n}.$$

Derive this result following the plan given below.

Outline of proof. Let $a_n = n!\, n^{-1/2} \left(\dfrac{e}{n} \right)^n$ $(n = 1, 2, \cdots)$.

Then

$$\frac{a_n}{a_{n+1}} = \frac{1}{e} \left(1 + \frac{1}{n} \right)^{n+1/2} \quad \text{and} \quad \ln \frac{a_n}{a_{n+1}} = \left(n + \frac{1}{2} \right) \ln \left(1 + \frac{1}{n} \right) - 1.$$

Show, in order, that:

(a) $\ln \left(1 + \dfrac{1}{n} \right) = \ln \left(\dfrac{1 + \dfrac{1}{2n + 1}}{1 - \dfrac{1}{2n + 1}} \right) = 2 \sum_0^\infty \dfrac{1}{(2k + 1)(2n + 1)^{2k+1}}.$

(b) $\ln \dfrac{a_n}{a_{n+1}} = \sum_0^\infty \dfrac{1}{(2k + 3)(2n + 1)^{2k+2}} < \dfrac{1}{3\,(2n + 1)^2} \sum_0^\infty \dfrac{1}{(2n + 1)^{2k}}.$

(c) $0 < \ln \dfrac{a_n}{a_{n+1}} < \dfrac{1}{12n\,(n + 1)}.$

HINT: Sum the geometric series in (b).
Thus,

$$\ln a_{n+1} < \ln a_n < \frac{1}{12n} - \frac{1}{12\,(n + 1)} + \ln a_{n+1}.$$

(d) Therefore,

$$x_n \equiv \ln a_n - \frac{1}{12n} < \ln a_{n+1} - \frac{1}{12\,(n + 1)} \equiv x_{n+1},$$

$y_n \equiv \ln a_n > y_{n+1},$ and $y_n > x_n$ so that

$$x_1 < \cdots < x_n < x_{n+1} < x_{n+2} < \cdots < y_{n+2} < y_{n+1} < y_n < \cdots < y_1.$$

Let $\lambda = $ l.u.b. $x_n = $ g.l.b. y_n. Then λ is well defined, and $\lim_{n \to \infty} a_n = e^\lambda$.

(e) Therefore,

$$\lim_{n \to \infty} a_n = \lim_{n \to \infty} \frac{a_n^2}{a_{2n}} = \lim_{n \to \infty} \left(\frac{2}{n} \right)^{1/2} \frac{2\cdot 4\cdot \cdots \cdot 2n}{1\cdot 3\cdot \cdots \cdot (2n - 1)} = (2\pi)^{1/2}.$$

[HINT: Use Wallis's inequality (6).]

(f)   Consequently, $a_n e^{-1/12n} < (2\pi)^{1/2} < a_n$
or
$$(2\pi n)^{1/2}(n/e)^n < n! < (2\pi n)^{1/2}(n/e)^n e^{1/12n}.$$

Can you improve this result and show that

$$n! > (2\pi n)^{1/2}\left(\frac{n}{e}\right)^n e^{1/12(n+1)}?$$

[REFERENCE: "Note on Stirling's formula" by T. S. Nanjundiah, *American Mathematical Monthly*, 66 (1959), pp. 701–703.]

31. Compute the first five Bernšteĭn polynomials for the function $\left|x - \tfrac{1}{2}\right|$ on [0,1]. Sketch their graphs and find $\max\limits_{[0,1]} \left|\,\left|x - \tfrac{1}{2}\right| - B_n(x)\right|$, $n = 0, 1, 2, 3$.

32. Let $f = \sin 2\pi x$. Compare the first four Bernšteĭn polynomials of f on [0,1] with the first four Taylor polynomials at $\tfrac{1}{2}$ of f.

33. If e is a rational number p/q, where p and q are positive whole numbers, then by Taylor's Theorem applied to e^x at $x = 1$

$$\frac{p}{q} = \sum_0^{q+2} \frac{1}{k!} + \frac{e^{\theta \cdot 1}}{(q+3)!},$$

where θ lies somewhere between 0 and 1. Prove that e is not a rational number, i.e., that e is irrational.

34. P. L. Čebyšev (1821–1894), a Russian mathematician, was the principal founder of the theory of approximation. A set of polynomials is named for him. Go to the library and find out what the Čebyšev polynomials are and why they are useful. NOTE: Westerners spell Čebyšev's name in a number of ways, often beginning with a T and ending with a double f. The correct pronunciation of his name, contrary to popular American custom, is Che-by-shoff′: *che* as in *check*, *by* roughly as in *be*, and *shoff* as in *sh* + *off*.

[4]

Three Modern Theorems

9. Power Means

The Isoperimetric Theorem is an ancient theorem that breathes life into mathematics even today. There can be no better test for modernity. The theorems we shall discuss in this chapter meet the same test; and, surprisingly enough, they are products of modern times. These theorems may be less celebrated than the Isoperimetric Theorem, but they play key rôles in several growing branches of mathematics and are in steady use. They were discovered by the nineteenth century mathematicians Cauchy, Bunyakovskiĭ, Hölder, and Minkowski.

Arithmetic and geometric means are special cases of power means, which are the means upon which the Cauchy, Hölder, and Minkowski inequalities are based.

Definition 10. The power mean, $\mathfrak{M}_r$, of order r of n positive numbers $a_1, \cdots, a_n$ is

$$\left(\frac{\sum\limits_{1}^{n} a_i^r}{n} \right)^{1/r} \qquad (r \neq 0).$$

A power mean, $\mathfrak{M}_1$, of order 1 is, of course, nothing but an arithmetic mean. Two other power means have special names: $\mathfrak{M}_{-1}$ is a *harmonic mean*, and $\mathfrak{M}_2$ is a *root mean square*. A geometric mean G_n is also denoted $\mathfrak{M}_0$. The reason for this is clear from the following computation.

$$\lim_{r \to 0} \mathfrak{M}_r(a_1, a_2) = \lim_{r \to 0} 2^{-1/r}(a_1 + a_2)^{1/r}$$

$$= a_1 \exp \left\{ \lim_{r \to 0} \frac{\ln [1 + (a_2/a_1)^r] - \ln 2}{r} \right\}$$

$$= a_1 \exp \left\{ \lim_{r \to 0} \frac{(a_2/a_1)^r \ln (a_2/a_1)}{1 + (a_2/a_1)^r} \right\} \quad \text{(L'Hôpital's Rule)}$$

$$= (a_1 a_2)^{1/2}$$

$$= G_2(a_1, a_2).$$

In addition to further justifying the choice of notation for G_n, the next theorem (which was proved by O. Schlömilch in 1858) compares the various power means of a fixed set of positive numbers.

Theorem 22. If $p < q$, then $\mathfrak{M}_p \leqq \mathfrak{M}_q$. Equality holds if and only if $a_1 = a_2 = \cdots = a_n$.

Proof. If q is positive, it is easy to show that $\mathfrak{M}_q \geqq \mathfrak{M}_0$. One simply observes that by Theorem 7,

$$\left(\prod_1^n a_i^q\right)^{1/n} \leqq \frac{\sum_1^n a_i^q}{n}.$$

Equality holds if and only if $a_1 = \cdots = a_n$. It follows from this inequality and Theorem 6 (extended to the case of real exponents) that $\mathfrak{M}_q \geqq \mathfrak{M}_0$, with equality holding if and only if $a_1 = \cdots = a_n$. If p is negative, the inequality $\mathfrak{M}_p \leqq \mathfrak{M}_0$ is similarly demonstrated. In particular we have shown that $\mathfrak{M}_{-1} \leqq \mathfrak{M}_1$, a result which can be written more elegantly as

$$\left(\sum_1^n a_i\right)\left(\sum_1^n \frac{1}{a_i}\right) \geqq n^2.$$

There are two cases yet to be considered: $0 < p < q$ and $p < q < 0$. We first assume that $0 < p < q$. It follows from the definition of $\mathfrak{M}_q$ that

$$\frac{\mathfrak{M}_q}{\mathfrak{M}_p} = \left(\frac{\sum_1^n \left(\frac{a_i}{\mathfrak{M}_p}\right)^q}{n}\right)^{1/q}.$$

Let

$$b_i = \left(\frac{a_i}{\mathfrak{M}_p}\right)^p \quad (i = 1, \cdots, n).$$

Then

(1)
$$\frac{\mathfrak{M}_q}{\mathfrak{M}_p} = \left(\frac{\sum_1^n b_i^{q/p}}{n}\right)^{1/q}.$$

We seek a helpful lower bound for $\sum_1^n b_i^{q/p}$. Such a bound may be obtained in the following way with the aid of Theorem 9. We first observe that since

$$\left(\frac{\sum_1^n b_i}{n}\right)^{1/p} = \frac{\mathfrak{M}_p}{\mathfrak{M}_p} = 1,$$

$$\sum_1^n b_i = n.$$

Now, by hypothesis, $q/p > 1$. Also, since b_i is positive, we can write $b_i = 1 + x_i$, where $x_i > -1$. Therefore,

$$\sum_1^n x_i = \sum_1^n b_i - \sum_1^n 1$$

$$= n - n$$

$$= 0.$$

By Theorem 9,

$$\sum_1^n (b_i)^{q/p} = \sum_1^n (1 + x_i)^{q/p} \geq \sum_1^n \left(1 + \frac{q}{p} x_i\right).$$

But

$$\sum_1^n \left(1 + \frac{q}{p} x_i\right) = n + \frac{q}{p} \sum_1^n x_i = n.$$

We can now conclude that

(2)
$$\sum_1^n b_i^{p/q} \geq n.$$

Equality holds if and only if $b_1 = b_2 = \cdots = b_n = 1$. The inequality

$$\frac{\mathfrak{M}_q}{\mathfrak{M}_p} \geq \left(\frac{n}{n}\right)^{1/q} = 1,$$

namely, the inequality $\mathfrak{M}_p \leq \mathfrak{M}_q$, follows from this result and (1). Equality holds if and only if $a_1 = a_2 = \cdots = a_n = \mathfrak{M}_p$.

To complete the proof of the theorem, we must consider the case $p < q < 0$. In this instance, $0 < q/p < 1$; hence, we obtain the inequality (2) with the sign of the inequality reversed:

$$\sum_1^n b_i^{q/p} \leq n.$$

Since q is negative, it follows that

$$\left(\sum_1^n b_i^{q/p}\right)^{1/q} \geq n^{1/q}.$$

Together with (1), this result leads to the desired inequality. Again, equality holds if and only if all the a_i's are equal. ∎

To conclude this section, we consider a simple, clever argument involving harmonic and geometric means. In 1954, D. K. Kazarinoff used them to obtain an improvement of Wallis's inequality (6) of §7 [*Edinburgh Mathematical Notes*, No. 40, pp. 19–21, 1956]. He considered the integral

$$J(\alpha) = \int_0^{\pi/2} \sin^\alpha x \, dx$$

for nonintegral values of α, and he was able to show by an elementary argument—it involves a function called the gamma function, and we omit it—that if $\alpha > -1$,

(3) $$J(\alpha) < \mathfrak{M}_{-1}[J(\alpha - 1), J(\alpha + 1)].$$

Now the geometric mean of two unequal positive numbers lies between them. Thus by (3),

(4) $$J(2n) < \mathfrak{M}_0\{J(2n), \mathfrak{M}_{-1}[J(2n - 1), J(2n + 1)]\} \quad (n = 1, 2, \cdots).$$

Let us adopt the notation

$$(2n)!! = 2 \cdot 4 \cdot 6 \cdots 2n$$

$$(2n + 1)!! = 1 \cdot 3 \cdot 5 \cdots (2n + 1).$$

Then, as we observed in §7,

$$J(2n) = \frac{(2n - 1)!!}{(2n)!!} \cdot \frac{\pi}{2} \quad \text{and} \quad J(2n + 1) = \frac{(2n)!!}{(2n + 1)!!} \quad (n = 1, 2, \cdots).$$

Therefore, the inequality (4) can be written in the form

$$\frac{(2n - 1)!!}{(2n)!!} < [(n + \tfrac{1}{4})\pi]^{-1/2} \quad (n = 1, 2, \cdots),$$

a result which improves one of the estimates in Wallis's Inequality.

In order to see that it might be useful to consider (3) for nonintegral values of α, let us consider it for $\alpha = 2n$ and try a proof by induction in this case. For $\alpha = 2n$, (3) may be written in the form

(5) $$\frac{\pi}{4} < \frac{[(2n)!!]^2(2n - 2)!!}{(2n - 1)!(2n - 1)!!(4n + 1)} = f(n).$$

When $n = 1$, this inequality becomes

$$\frac{\pi}{4} < \frac{2^2 \cdot 1}{1 \cdot 1 \cdot 5} = \frac{4}{5},$$

which is obviously correct. Suppose that (5) holds for $n = k$. If $n = k + 1$, the right-hand member, $f(k + 1)$, is

$$f(k) \cdot \frac{(2k + 2)^2(4k + 1)}{(2k + 1)^2(4k + 5)}$$

or

$$f(k) \cdot \frac{16k^3 + 36k^2 + 24k + 4}{16k^3 + 36k^2 + 24k + 5},$$

which is, alas, a wee bit smaller than $f(k)$ so that the inequality

$$\frac{\pi}{4} < f(k+1)$$

is not at all obvious if one only knows that

$$\frac{\pi}{4} < f(k).$$

10. The Cauchy, Bunyakovskiĭ, Hölder, and Minkowski Inequalities

Theorem 23. (*Hölder's Inequality*). If x and y are positive, if $x + y = 1$, and if the numbers $a_1, \cdots, a_n$ and $b_1, \cdots, b_n$ are nonnegative, then

$$(6) \qquad \sum_1^n a_i^x b_i^y \leq \left(\sum_1^n a_i\right)^x \cdot \left(\sum_1^n b_i\right)^y,$$

or equivalently

$$(7) \qquad \sum_1^n a_i b_i \leq \left(\sum_1^n a_i^{1/x}\right)^x \cdot \left(\sum_1^n b_i^{1/y}\right)^y.$$

Equality holds in (6) if and only if $b_1 = b_2 = \cdots = b_n = 0$ or

$$\frac{a_1}{b_1} = \frac{a_2}{b_2} = \cdots = \frac{a_n}{b_n}.$$

The special case

$$\sum_1^n a_i b_i \leq \left[\left(\sum_1^n a_i^2\right)\left(\sum_1^n b_i^2\right)\right]^{1/2}$$

of (7) is known as Cauchy's Inequality. He published it in 1821. Hölder's generalization appeared in 1889 ["Über einen Mittelwertsatz," *Göttinger Nachrichten*, pp. 38–47, 1889]. Cauchy's Inequality may be interpreted geometrically as follows. Divide both sides by the right-hand member, and consider the angle formed by the vectors $(a_1, \cdots, a_n)$ and $(b_1, \cdots, b_n)$. (If it makes you more comfortable, assume that $n = 3$.) The cosine of this angle is precisely the left-hand member of the transformed Cauchy Inequality, which thus says that the cosine of an angle may not exceed 1.

Proof of Theorem 23. We shall derive (7). If either $a_1 = a_2 = \cdots = a_n = 0$ or $b_1 = b_2 = \cdots = b_n = 0$, (7) is obviously correct. Henceforth we may therefore assume that neither alternative holds. Let us write the inequality (1′) of §4 in the form

$$(8) \qquad y^m \leq 1 + m(y - 1) \quad (y > 0 \quad \text{and} \quad 0 < m < 1).$$

Suppose for the moment that $y = A/B$, where A and B are positive. Then by (8),

$$A^m B^{1-m} \leq B + m(A - B) \quad (0 < m < 1);$$

or, since we may replace m by x and $1 - m$ by y,

$$(9) \qquad\qquad A^x B^y \leq xA + yB.$$

Equality holds if and only if $A = B$. Inequality (9) is almost Hölder's inequality. (If $x = y = \frac{1}{2}$, note that (9) reduces to the Theorem of Arithmetic and Geometric Means with $n = 2$.)

Now let

$$A_i = \frac{a_i^{1/x}}{\sum\limits_1^n a_i^{1/x}}, \quad B_i = \frac{b_i^{1/y}}{\sum\limits_1^n b_i^{1/y}},$$

and consider $\sum\limits_1^n A_i^x B_i^y$. It follows from (9) and the definitions of A_i and B_i that

$$\sum_1^n A_i^x B_i^y \leq x \sum_1^n A_i + y \sum_1^n B_i = x + y = 1,$$

or

$$\sum_1^n a_i b_i \leq \left(\sum_1^n a_i^{1/x} \right)^x \left(\sum_1^n b_i^{1/y} \right)^y.$$

Equality holds if and only if

$$\frac{a_i^{1/x}}{\sum\limits_1^n a_i^{1/x}} = \frac{b_i^{1/y}}{\sum\limits_1^n b_i^{1/y}} \quad (i = 1, \cdots, n),$$

that is, if and only if

$$\frac{a_1^y}{b_1^x} = \frac{a_2^y}{b_2^x} = \cdots = \frac{a_n^y}{b_n^x}.$$

Inequality (6) can be obtained from (7) by replacing a_i by a_i^x and b_i by b_i^y in (7). ∎

PROBLEM

35. Give an alternative derivation of Cauchy's Inequality, and show that it holds for any real numbers whatsoever be their sign. HINT: Consider either

$$\phi(t) = \sum_1^n (a_i + b_i t)^2 \quad \text{or} \quad \sum_{i=1}^n \sum_{j=1}^n (a_i b_j - a_j b_i)^2.$$

A third basic inequality in modern analysis was discovered by the great geometer Hermann Minkowski (1864–1909). It is a generalization of that simplest of observations about Euclidean space, namely, that the straight-line distance is the shortest one between two points. Let $m + 1$ points $X_1 = (x_1^1, \cdots, x_n^1), \cdots, X_{m+1} = (x_1^{m+1}, \cdots, x_n^{m+1})$ be given in Euclidean n-space. (Again assume $n = 3$ if it makes you more comfortable.) The distance from X_1 to X_{m+1} is certainly less than or equal to the sum $\sum_1^m \overline{X_j X_{j+1}}$ of the distances from X_j to X_{j+1} $(j = 1, \cdots, m)$; that is,

$$\left[\sum_{k=1}^n (x_1^k - x_{m+1}^k)^2 \right]^{1/2} \le \sum_{j=1}^m \left[\sum_{k=1}^n (x_j^k - x_{j+1}^k)^2 \right]^{1/2}.$$

If we let $u_{jk} = x_j^k - x_{j+1}^k$, then this inequality becomes

(10)
$$\left[\sum_{k=1}^n \left(\sum_{j=1}^m u_{jk} \right)^2 \right]^{1/2} \le \sum_{j=1}^m \left[\sum_{k=1}^n u_{jk}^2 \right]^{1/2}.$$

This is a special case of Minkowski's Inequality. (The above argument based on geometric intuition is not a proof.) Equality holds if and only if the points $X_1, \cdots, X_{m+1}$ lie on one straight line, that is, if and only if

$$\frac{u_{j,k}}{u_{j+1,k}} = \frac{u_{j,k+1}}{u_{j+1,k+1}} = c_j \quad (j = 1, \cdots, m - 1; k = 1, \cdots, n - 1)$$

where c_j depends only on j.

PROBLEM

36. (Lhuilier). Let T be a tetrahedron with volume V, surface area S, base area A, and base perimeter P. Suppose T_0 is a right tetrahedron (the foot of the altitude to the base is the center of its circumcircle), and suppose that $V = V_0$, $A = A_0$, and $P \ge P_0$, where V_0, A_0, P_0, and S_0 are the volume, base area, etc. of T_0. Use (10) to show that $S \ge S_0$. When is equality attained? HINT:

$$S - A = \sum_1^3 \tfrac{1}{2} a_j (p_j + h^2)^{1/2},$$

where a_1, a_2, a_3 are the lengths of the sides of the base of T, p_1, p_2, p_3 are the perpendiculars from the center of the circumcircle of the base to its sides, and h is the altitude on the base. (Why?) Also,

$$S_0 - A_0 = \tfrac{1}{2} (4A_0^2 + h^2 P_0^2)^{1/2}. \quad \text{(Why?)}$$

What can you show if T is a pyramid with an n-gon for a base, and T_0 is a right pyramid?

We now prove a theorem containing (10) as a special case.

Theorem 24. (*Minkowski's Inequality*). If the numbers u_{jk} $(j = 1, \cdots, m; k = 1, \cdots, n)$ are nonnegative, and if p is a real number greater than or equal to 1, then

$$(11) \qquad \left[\sum_{k=1}^{n} \left(\sum_{j=1}^{m} u_{jk} \right)^{p} \right]^{1/p} \leq \sum_{j=1}^{m} \left[\sum_{k=1}^{n} u_{jk}^{p} \right]^{1/p} ;$$

if $0 < p < 1$, then

$$(12) \qquad \left[\sum_{k=1}^{n} \left(\sum_{j=1}^{m} u_{jk} \right)^{p} \right]^{1/p} \geq \sum_{j=1}^{m} \left[\sum_{k=1}^{n} u_{jk}^{p} \right]^{1/p} .$$

In both cases equality holds if and only if the numbers in sets $(u_{11}, \cdots, u_{1n}), \cdots, (u_{m1}, \cdots, u_{mn})$ are proportional.

Proof. We shall prove the theorem only in the case $m = 2$ and $p > 1$. (The case $p = 1$ is trivial, and the case $m > 2$ will be discussed below.) In the case $m = 2$ we shall write A_k for u_{1k} and B_k for u_{2k}, so that the inequality we wish to prove is

$$\left[\sum_{1}^{n} (A_k + B_k)^{p} \right]^{1/p} \leq \left(\sum_{1}^{n} A_k^{p} \right)^{1/p} + \left(\sum_{1}^{n} B_k^{p} \right)^{1/p} \quad (p > 1).$$

Let $1/q = 1 - 1/p$, let $A_k = a_k$ and $(A_k + B_k)^{p/q} = b_k$ in (7), and let $x = 1/p$ there. Then

$$(13) \qquad \sum_{1}^{n} A_k(A_k + B_k)^{p/q} \leq \left(\sum_{1}^{n} A_k^{p} \right)^{1/p} \left[\sum_{1}^{n} (A_k + B_k)^{p} \right]^{1/q} .$$

Similarly,

$$(14) \qquad \sum_{1}^{n} B_k(A_k + B_k)^{p/q} \leq \left(\sum_{1}^{n} B_k^{p} \right)^{1/p} \left[\sum_{1}^{n} (A_k + B_k)^{p} \right]^{1/q} .$$

Equality holds if and only if $B_1 = B_2 = \cdots = B_n = 0$ or

$$(15) \qquad \frac{A_1}{B_1} = \cdots = \frac{A_n}{B_n} .$$

Since $p = 1 + p/q$,

$$(A_k + B_k)^{p} = (A_k + B_k)(A_k + B_k)^{p/q}.$$

Therefore, by (13) and (14),

$$\sum_{1}^{n} (A_k + B_k)^{p} \leq \left[\left(\sum_{1}^{n} A_k^{p} \right)^{1/p} + \left(\sum_{1}^{n} B_k^{p} \right)^{1/p} \right] \left[\sum_{1}^{n} (A_k + B_k)^{p} \right]^{1/q} ;$$

or since $\dfrac{1}{p} + \dfrac{1}{q} = 1$,

$$\left[\sum_{1}^{n} (A_k + B_k)^{p} \right]^{1/p} \leq \left(\sum_{1}^{n} A_k^{p} \right)^{1/p} + \left(\sum_{1}^{n} B_k^{p} \right)^{1/p} .$$

The condition for equality is (15).∎

In order to prove Theorem 24 when $m > 2$, one may generalize **(9)** to the case of

$$(16) \qquad A_1^{x_1} A_2^{x_2} \cdots A_m^{x_m} \leqq \sum_1^m x_i A_i,$$

where $\sum_1^m x_i = 1$ and each x_i is positive.

PROBLEM

37. Perform this generalization. {Can you use induction to establish Minkowski's Inequality for $m > 2$?} HINT: If the x_i are rational write the numbers x_i in the form y_i/N $(i = 1, \cdots, m)$, where y_i and N are integers, and apply Theorem 7.

You will find Minkowski's Inequality in his remarkable book, *Geometrie der Zahlen*, I, pp. 115–117 (Leipzig, 1896).

Many of the most important applications of the Hölder and Minkowski Inequalities have to do with complex numbers. We therefore state one of them in this case.

Hölder's Inequality for complex numbers. If $p > 1$ and $\dfrac{1}{p} + \dfrac{1}{q} = 1$, then

$$\left| \sum_1^n a_i b_i \right| \leqq \left(\sum_1^n |a_i|^p \right)^{1/p} \left(\sum_1^n |b_i|^q \right)^{1/q}.$$

Equality holds if and only if $|a_i|^p / |b_i|^q$ is a constant independent of i and the argument of $a_i b_i$ is independent of i.

The proof is almost the same as when the a_i's and b_i's are real. We need only note that $\left| \sum_1^n a_i b_i \right| < \sum_1^n |a_i b_i|$ unless the argument of $a_i b_i$ is independent of i.

Analogues of the Cauchy, Hölder, and Minkowski Inequalities in which integration takes the role of finite summation are the forms of these inequalities that are currently most used. Let us first of all consider Bunyakovskiĭ's analogue of Cauchy's Inequality. (Western writers often refer to this as Schwarz's Inequality. Schwarz ["Über ein die Flächen kleinsten Flächeninhalts betreffendes Problem der Variationsrechnung," *Acta soc. scient. Fenn.* 15 (1885), pp. 315–362] obtained the same result long after Bunyakovskiĭ ["Sur quelques inégalités concernant les intégrales ordinaires et les intégrales aux différences finies," *Mémoires de l'Acad. de St. Pétersbourg* (VII), 1859, No. 9]. But in the nineteenth century little attention was paid to scientific activity in Russia, and contributions of fundamental importance were overlooked. [The present one is an almost trivial extension of Cauchy's work and the lion's share of credit belongs to him]. A good compromise is to call the result the CBS-Inequality.)

Theorem 25.   (*The CBS-Inequality*).   If f and g are Riemann-integrable real-valued functions on $[a,b]$, then

(17) $$\left| \int_a^b f(x)g(x)\,dx \right| \leq \left[\int_a^b f^2(x)\,dx \right]^{1/2} \left[\int_a^b g^2(x)\,dx \right]^{1/2}.$$

Proof.   It is clear that for any real number y,

$$F(y) \equiv \int_a^b [yf(x) + g(x)]^2\,dx \geq 0.$$

If $\int_a^b f^2(x)\,dx = 0$, then $f \equiv 0$, and (17) is obvious.   Otherwise,

$$F\left(\dfrac{-\displaystyle\int_a^b f(t)g(t)\,dt}{\displaystyle\int_a^b f^2(s)\,ds} \right)$$

$$= \dfrac{\left(\displaystyle\int_a^b f^2(y)\,dy\right)\left(\displaystyle\int_a^b g^2(v)\,dv\right) - \left(\displaystyle\int_a^b f(x)g(x)\,dx\right)^2}{\displaystyle\int_a^b f^2(t)\,dt} \geq 0.$$

Thus,

$$\left(\int_a^b f^2(x)\,dx\right)\left(\int_a^b g^2(t)\,dt\right) - \left(\int_a^b f(s)g(s)\,ds\right)^2 \geq 0.\blacksquare$$

When does equality hold?

Theorem 26.   (*Hölder's Inequality*).   If f and g are continuous real-valued functions defined on $[a,b]$, if $p > 1$, and if

$$\frac{1}{p} + \frac{1}{q} = 1,$$

then

(18) $$\left| \int_a^b f(t)g(t)\,dt \right| \leq \int_a^b |f(t)g(t)|\,dt$$

$$\leq \left(\int_a^b |f(s)|^p\,ds\right)^{1/p} \left(\int_a^b |g(t)|^q\,dt\right)^{1/q}.$$

Equality holds if and only if at least one of f and g is identically zero or $f \cdot g$ does not change sign on $[a,b]$ and there exist positive constants α and β such that $\alpha|f|^p \equiv \beta|g|^q$ on $[a,b]$.

Proof. If one of f and g is identically zero, **(18)** clearly holds. If neither f nor g is identically zero, set $x = 1/p$, $y = 1/q$,

$$A = \frac{|f(t)|^p}{\displaystyle\int_a^b |f(t)|^p \, dt}, \quad \text{and} \quad B = \frac{|g(t)|^q}{\displaystyle\int_a^b |g(t)|^q \, dt}$$

in **(9)**, and integrate from a to b. It follows that

$$\frac{\displaystyle\int_a^b |f(t)g(t)| \, dt}{\left[\displaystyle\int_a^b |f(t)|^p \, dt\right]^{1/p} \left[\displaystyle\int_a^b |g(t)|^q \, dt\right]^{1/q}} \leq \frac{1}{p} \cdot \frac{\displaystyle\int_a^b |f(t)|^p \, dt}{\displaystyle\int_a^b |f(t)|^p \, dt} + \frac{1}{q} \cdot \frac{\displaystyle\int_a^b |g(t)|^q \, dt}{\displaystyle\int_a^b |g(t)|^q \, dt}$$

$$= \frac{1}{p} \cdot 1 + \frac{1}{q} \cdot 1$$

$$= 1.$$

Equality holds if and only if $A = B$, that is, if and only if

$$\left(\int_a^b |g(t)|^q \, dt\right) |f|^p = \left(\int_a^b |f(t)|^p \, dt\right) |g|^q.$$

The derivation of the remaining condition for equality is left as miscellaneous Problem 39. ∎

It is obvious that both Theorems 25 and 26 hold if f and g are complex-valued functions, except that the conditions for equality are more complicated.

PROBLEM

38. Use **(16)** to generalize Theorem 26.

Theorem 27. (*Minkowski's Inequality*). If f and g are continuous real-valued functions and if $p \geq 1$, then

$$\left[\int_a^b |f(t) + g(t)|^p \, dt\right]^{1/p} \leq \left[\int_a^b |f(t)|^p \, dt\right]^{1/p} + \left[\int_a^b |g(t)|^p \, dt\right]^{1/p}.$$

PROBLEMS

39. Prove Theorem 27. When does equality hold?

40. Use the result of Problem 38 to generalize Theorem 27.

There are numerous inequalities related to those which we have discussed in this chapter, and still further generalizations and extensions of the above theorems can be made. A reader who wishes to study these generalizations and related inequalities seriously should read *Inequalities* by G. H. Hardy, J. E. Littlewood, and G. Pólya (Cambridge Univ. Press, 1934). Although the text of this pamphlet ceases at this point, an important portion of the pamphlet lies ahead. I am sure you will learn much more by solving the remaining problems than you can by reading my inadequate explanations. The problems immediately below are in part applications of the material covered in this chapter and in part suggestive of theories in which the inequalities which we have met have been of great value.

PROBLEMS

41. Show that

(a) $\dfrac{1}{51} < \displaystyle\int_0^1 x^{50} e^x \, dx < \left(\dfrac{1}{101}\right)^{1/2} \left(\dfrac{e^2 - 1}{2}\right)^{1/2} < \dfrac{1}{5}$,

(b) $\dfrac{5}{4} < \displaystyle\int_0^1 (1 + x)^{2/3}(1 + x^3)^{1/3} \, dx < \left(\dfrac{3}{2}\right)^{2/3} \left(\dfrac{5}{4}\right)^{1/3} < \dfrac{3}{2}$,

(c) $\dfrac{4}{3} < \displaystyle\int_0^1 (1 + x^3)^{4/3} \, dx < [1 + 5^{-3/4}]^{4/3}$.

42. Definition. An infinite sequence $\{a_i\}$ of real numbers is an element of the space l_2 if and only if $\displaystyle\sum_1^\infty a_i^2$ converges.

We write $\mathbf{a} = \{a_i\}$, $\mathbf{0} = \{0\}$; and we call the number $\left(\displaystyle\sum_1^\infty a_i^2\right)^{1/2}$, which we denote $\|\mathbf{a}\|$, the norm of $\mathbf{a}$. If $\mathbf{a}$ and $\mathbf{b}$ are elements of l_2, prove the following.

(a) For any real number k, $k\mathbf{a}$ is in l_2. (We define $k\mathbf{a} = \{ka_i\}$.) Moreover,

$$\|k\mathbf{a}\| = |k| \cdot \|\mathbf{a}\|.$$

(b) $\|\mathbf{a}\| \geq 0$, and $\|\mathbf{a}\| = 0$ if and only if $\mathbf{a} = \mathbf{0}$.

(c) Define $\mathbf{a} + \mathbf{b}$ to be $\{a_i + b_i\}$. Then $\mathbf{a} + \mathbf{b}$ is in l_2, and

$$\|\mathbf{a} + \mathbf{b}\| \leq \|\mathbf{a}\| + \|\mathbf{b}\|.$$

Moreover, $\|\mathbf{a} - \mathbf{b}\| = \|\mathbf{b} - \mathbf{a}\|$; and if $\mathbf{c}$ is in l_2,

$$\|\mathbf{a} - \mathbf{b}\| \leq \|\mathbf{a} - \mathbf{c}\| + \|\mathbf{c} - \mathbf{b}\|.$$

Thus we can interpret $\|\mathbf{a} - \mathbf{b}\|$ as the distance between the points $\mathbf{a}$ and $\mathbf{b}$ in l_2. The space l_2 is called a *metric space* for this reason, and the inequality $\|\mathbf{a} + \mathbf{b}\| \leq \|\mathbf{a}\| + \|\mathbf{b}\|$ is known as the triangle inequality. Note the analogy between the notion of absolute value or distance in Euclidean space and the notion of norm in l_2. One may think of l_2 as a Euclidean space with infinitely many dimensions. The analogy between Euclidean spaces and l_2 can be extended still further. A scalar product of two elements in l_2 can be defined in analogy with the notion of the scalar product of two vectors in three-dimensional Euclidean space; namely, we define

$$(\mathbf{a}, \mathbf{b}) = \sum_1^\infty a_i b_i.$$

(d) Prove that $\sum_1^\infty a_i b_i$ converges (in fact, it converges absolutely), and thereby show that the scalar product of any two elements of l_2 is well defined. The number

$$\frac{(\mathbf{a},\mathbf{b})}{\|\mathbf{a}\| \cdot \|\mathbf{b}\|}$$

is called the cosine of the angle θ between the vectors $\mathbf{a}$ and $\mathbf{b}$ (Fig. 28).

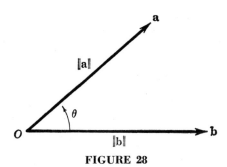

FIGURE 28

Show that $|\cos \theta| \leq 1$.

The first man to find and use the properties of the space l_2 was David Hilbert. l_2 is called a Hilbert space in his honor.

43. Who was David Hilbert, and why is he famous?

44. State and prove the CBS-Inequality for multiple integrals.

45. Let f be a nonnegative continuous function defined on $[a,b]$. Let

$$\mathfrak{M}_r(f) = \left[\frac{\int_a^b f^r(s)\, ds}{b - a}\right]^{1/r}.$$

Prove that $\min_{[a,b]} f < \mathfrak{M}_r(f) < \max_{[a,b]} f$ unless f is constant.

46. Let $\mathcal{G}(f) = \exp\left[\dfrac{\int_a^b \ln f\, dx}{b - a}\right]$. $\mathcal{G}(f)$ is called the geometric mean of f. Prove that

$$\mathcal{G}(f) \leq \mathfrak{M}_1(f) \equiv \mathcal{A}(f)$$

and that equality holds only if f is constant.

47. Prove that if $r > 0$, then

$$\mathcal{G}(f) \leq \mathfrak{M}_r(f);$$

and prove that equality holds if and only if f is constant.

48. Show that $\mathcal{G}(f) + \mathcal{G}(g) \leq \mathcal{G}(f + g)$. When does equality hold?

49. Prove that $\lim\limits_{r \to 0^+} \mathfrak{M}_r(f) = \mathfrak{G}(f)$.   ($r \to 0^+$ means r approaches zero only through positive values.) Thus we may write $\mathfrak{M}_0(f) = \mathfrak{G}(f)$.

HINT: $e^x > 1 + x$ for all x; therefore, $e^{x-1} > x$. Thus, $\ln x < x - 1$ if $x > 0$. Show that $\ln \mathfrak{G}(f) \leq \dfrac{1}{r} \ln \mathfrak{A}(f^r)$.

50. Prove that, if $r > s > 0$, then $\mathfrak{M}_r(f) \geq \mathfrak{M}_s(f)$. Equality holds if and only if f is constant.

51. (H. Weyl). Prove that if the integrals below exist and if f is real-valued, then

$$\int_{-\infty}^{\infty} f^2(x)\, dx < 2 \left[\int_{-\infty}^{\infty} x^2 f^2(x)\, dx \right]^{1/2} \left[\int_{-\infty}^{\infty} f'^2(x)\, dx \right]^{1/2}$$

unless $f = \alpha e^{-\beta x^2}$.   HINT: Use Hölder's Inequality.

52. Definition. Let f be a real-valued function defined on $[a,b]$ and continuous on $[a,b]$ except at a finite number of points. f is in the space $I_2(a,b)$ if and only if

$$\int_a^b f^2(x)\, dx$$

converges.

For example, $x^{-1/4}$ is in $I_2(0,1)$, but $x^{-1/2}$ is not. Either one of a and b may be chosen to be $\pm\infty$. Thus e^{-x^2} is in $L_2(-\infty, \infty)$, but e^{x^2} and x are not. Let us call the number $\left[\int_a^b f^2(x)\, dx \right]^{1/2}$ the I_2 norm of f (or more simply, the norm of f), and let us denote it $\|f\|$. Prove that

   (a) If f and g are in $I_2(a,b)$, then $f + g$, $f \cdot g$, and kf (k a real number) are all in $I_2(a,b)$.

   (b) $\|f\| \geq 0$, and $\|f\| = 0$ if and only if $f \equiv 0$.

   (c) $\|kf\| = |k| \cdot \|f\|$.

   (d) $\|f + g\| \leq \|f\| + \|g\|$.

Thus, we may consider $\|f - g\|$ as the distance between the points f and g of $I_2(a,b)$ and call $I_2(a,b)$ a metric space. Note that $\|f - g\| = \|g - f\|$ and $\|f - g\| \leq \|f - h\| + \|h - g\|$.

53. If the points x_n ($n = 1, 2, 3, \cdots$) are in one-dimensional Euclidean space E^1 (that is, the real line) and if, given any $\epsilon > 0$, there is an integer N depending only on ϵ, such that

$$|x_n - x_m| < \epsilon$$

wherever n and m are greater than N, then $\lim\limits_{n \to \infty} x_n$ exists, and this limit is in E^1. Such a sequence is called a Cauchy sequence. However, as we have defined the space I_2, it is not true that if the functions f_n ($n = 1, 2, 3, \cdots$) are in I_2 and if, given any $\epsilon > 0$, there is an integer N depending only on ϵ, such that $\|f_n - f_m\| < \epsilon$ provided $n > m > N$, then the sequence $\{f_n\}$ converges to a function in I_2. Can you construct an example of this phenomenon? Because of this unhappy state of affairs it is necessary to generalize the notion of integration and to introduce the process called Lebesgue integration after its creator, Henri Lebesgue. If $\|f\|$ is interpreted in the context of Lebesgue integration, then the resulting extension of the space $I_2(a,b)$ is called $L_2(a,b)$. A Cauchy sequence of functions in $L_2(a,b)$ always converges to a function in $L_2(a,b)$. The space L_2, defined in terms of the Lebesgue integral, is one of the most important mathematical spaces; for example, it is the proper setting for the theory of Fourier series.

A metric space in which a scalar product has been defined and which is such that every Cauchy sequence of elements of the space converges to an element of the space is said to be a Hilbert space. Thus, $L_2(a,b)$ is a Hilbert space if it is properly defined—$(f,g) = \int_a^b f(x)g(x)\,dx$.

54. Definition. An infinite sequence $\{a_i\}$ of real numbers is an element of the space l_p $(p > 1)$ if and only if $\sum_1^\infty |a_i|^p$ converges. $\|a\|$ is defined to be $\left[\sum_1^\infty |a_i|^p\right]^{1/p}$.

Show that l_p has properties analogous to those of l_2.

MISCELLANEOUS PROBLEMS

Prove the following assertions.

1. If x, y, and z are positive, and if $x^4 + y^4 + z^4 = 27$, then $x + y + z \leq 3\sqrt{3}$.

2. $|a \sin x + b \cos x| \leq (|a|^2 + |b|^2)^{1/2}$.

3. If $x > 0$ and if $n > 1$, then $x/(n + x) < (x + 1)^{1/n} - 1 < x/n$.

4. $\left||x|^{1/n} - |y|^{1/n}\right| \leq |x - y|^{1/n}$.

5. If $0 \leq x \leq 1$,
$$\frac{|x|}{1 + |x|} \leq \ln(1 + x) \leq \frac{|x|(1 + |x|)}{|1 + x|}.$$

6. If $0 < x < \pi/2$, $2x + x \cos x - 3 \sin x > 0$.

7. If $\alpha + \beta + \gamma = \pi$, $\tan^2(\alpha/2) + \tan^2(\beta/2) + \tan^2(\gamma/2) \geq 1$.

8. $xyz(x + y + z) \leq x^2y^2 + y^2z^2 + z^2x^2$.

9. If $x \geq y \geq z > 0$, $8xyz \leq (x + y)(y + z)(z + x)$.

10. If $x \geq y > 0$, $(x + y)(x^3 + y^3)(x^7 + y^7) \leq 4(x^{11} + y^{11})$.

11. If $x \geq y \geq z > 0$,
$$\frac{1}{x} + \frac{1}{y} + \frac{1}{z} \geq \frac{9}{x + y + z}.$$

12. If $x + y = 1$ and if $x \geq y > 0$, then $(x + x^{-1})^2 + (y + y^{-1})^2 \geq \frac{25}{4}$.

13. $(x^2 + y^2)^{1/2} \leq |x| + 2|y| \leq [5(x^2 + y^2)]^{1/2}$.

14. If $x^3 + y^3 = z^3$ and if x, y, and x are positive, then $(xy/z^2)^3 \leq \frac{1}{4}$.

15. If $x > 0$, $x^{1/4} \leq 2x + \frac{3}{8}$.

16. If $0 < x < 1/n$, $n = 1, 2, \cdots$, then $(1 + x)^n < (1 - nx)^{-1}$.

17. (Čebyšev). If $a_1 \geq a_2 \geq \cdots \geq a_n \geq 0$ and if $b_1 \geq b_2 \geq \cdots \geq b_n \geq 0$, then

$$\frac{1}{n}\sum_1^n a_k b_k \geq \left(\frac{1}{n}\sum_1^n a_k\right)\left(\frac{1}{n}\sum_1^n b_k\right) \quad (n = 1, 2, \cdots).$$

18. If $x > 0$,

$$1 \geq \frac{\sum_0^{n-1}(k+1)x^k}{\sum_0^{n-1}(k+1)^2 x^k} \geq \frac{1}{n}.$$

19. If $n > 100$, then $0 < 1 - \cos(1/n) < \frac{1}{2}\cdot 10^{-4}$.

20. If $x > e^{10^3}$, then $x^{1/100} > \ln x$.

21. If $p > 0$, there is an $N > 0$ such that $x^p > \ln x$ provided $x > N$.

22. If p and q are positive, there is an N such that $e^{x^p} > x^q$ provided $x > N$.

23. If $p > 1$ and $|x| \neq |y|$, then $2^{p-1}(|x|^p + |y|^p) > (|x| + |y|)^p$.

24. If $p > 1$, $n^{p-1}\sum_1^n |x_i|^p > \left(\sum_1^n |x_i|\right)^p$ unless $|x_1| = |x_2| = \cdots = |x_n|$.

25. If $a \geq b > 0$, $a^a b^b \geq \dfrac{(a+b)^{a+b}}{2}$.

26. (H. Bohr). If $c > 0$, $|a + b|^2 \leq (1 + c)|a|^2 + \left(1 + \dfrac{1}{c}\right)|b|^2$.

27. (J. Berkes). If $x_i > 0$ and $\sum_0^n (1 + x_i)^{-1} \geq n$, then

$$\prod_0^n x_i^{-1} \geq n^{n+1} \quad (n = 1, 2, \cdots).$$

28. If $a_i > 0$ and $x_1 \leq x_2 \leq x_3 \leq \cdots \leq x_n$, then

$$x_1 \leq \frac{\sum_1^n a_i x_i}{\sum_1^n a_i} \leq x_n.$$

29. If $x > 0$, $\ln(1 + x) \leq x(1 - x)^{-1}$.

30. (a) $\dfrac{n}{2} < \sum_1^{2^n-1}\dfrac{1}{k} < n \quad (n = 1, 2, \cdots)$.

(b) $\left\{\sum_1^n \dfrac{1}{k} - \ln n\right\}$ is a monotone sequence.

(c) $\sum_1^n \dfrac{k}{(k+1)!} < 1 \quad (n = 1, 2, \cdots)$.

(d) $\sum_0^n \dfrac{1}{k!} < e < \sum_0^n \dfrac{1}{k!} + \dfrac{1}{n!n} \quad (n = 1, 2, \cdots)$.

31. (Lambek and Moser). Let a, b, h, r, and s be natural numbers. Let $h(n) = \sum_1^n \frac{1}{k}$, and let $l_r(a) = h(ra) - h(r)$. Then

(a) $\dfrac{a}{a+b} \le h(a+b) - h(b) \le \dfrac{a}{b}$.

(b) $0 < l_{r+1}(a) - l_r(a) < \dfrac{1}{r(r+1)}$.

(c) $0 \le l_s(a) - l_r(a) \le \dfrac{1}{r} - \dfrac{1}{s}$ $(r < s)$.

(d) $0 \le l_r(ab) - l_r(a) - l_r(b) < \dfrac{1}{r}$.

(e) $\dfrac{1}{a+1} \le l_r(a+1) - l_r(a) < \dfrac{1}{r}$.

32. A *continued fraction*

$$a_0 + \cfrac{b_1}{a_1 + \cfrac{b_2}{a_2 + \cdots \cfrac{b_n}{a_n + \cdots}}}$$

is sometimes denoted $Fc(a_0, b_1\colon a_1, b_2\colon a_2, \cdots, b_n\colon a_n \cdots)$. Let $A_0 = a_0$, $B_0 = 1$, $A_1 = a_1 A_0 + b_1 B_1 = a_1 B_0$, and let

$$A_n = a_n A_{n-1} + b_n A_{n-2},$$

$$B_n = a_n B_{n-1} + b_n B_{n-2} \quad (n = 2, 3, \cdots).$$

(a) $A_n/B_n = Fc(a_0, b_1\colon a_1, b_2\colon a_2, \cdots, b_n\colon a_n)$.

(b) $A_n B_{n-1} - A_{n-1} B_n = (-1)^{n-1} \prod_1^n b_i$.

(c) If the a_i's and b_i's are positive, $\{A_{2n}/B_{2n}\}$ is a monotone increasing sequence and $\{A_{2n+1}/B_{2n+1}\}$ is a monotone decreasing sequence.

(d) Can you find a continued fraction which represents $\sqrt{2}$?

33. $\sum_1^n \dfrac{1}{k^2} + \dfrac{1}{n+1} < \dfrac{\pi^2}{6} = \sum_1^\infty \dfrac{1}{k^2} < \sum_1^n \dfrac{1}{k^2} + \dfrac{1}{n}$.

34. If $0 < a_1 \le a_2 \le \cdots \le a_n$ and p is positive, then

$$a_n \le \left(\sum_1^n a_i^p \right)^{1/p} \le a_n n^{1/p}.$$

35. $|\sin x - \sin y| < |x - y|$ unless $x = y$. (Thus, the sine function is continuous.)

36. $x^{10} + 3x - 7 = 0$ has at most two real roots.

37. If $0 \le x \le y < \pi/2$, then

$$x \ge \sin x \ge \frac{2}{\pi} x, \quad \text{and} \quad (y - x) \sec^2 x \le \tan y - \tan x \le (y - x) \sec^2 y.$$

38. If x and y are positive, $e^x > \left(1 + \dfrac{x}{y} \right)^y$.

39. If f is continuous on $[a,b]$, $\left| \int_a^b f(t)\, dt \right| < \int_a^b |f(t)|\, dt$ unless f does not change sign on $[a,b]$.

40. If $ab \neq 0$, then

$$\int_0^\pi \frac{\sin t\, dt}{\sqrt{a^2 + b^2 - 2ab \cos t}} = \frac{|a+b| - |a-b|}{ab} = \frac{2}{\max\,(|a|,\,|b|)}.$$

41. Let p_n be the nth prime. $\sum_1^\infty p_n^{-1}$ diverges. Convince yourself that the following lines do indeed constitute a proof of this remarkable assertion. Incidentally, it is a consequence of this theorem that the number of primes is infinite. (Euclid's proof is simpler.)

Proof. (E. Dux). Suppose $\sum_1^\infty p_n^{-1}$ converges. Then if k is chosen large enough (k fixed),

$$\sum_k^\infty p_r^{-1} = q < 1.$$

Having chosen k, we divide the natural numbers into three classes as follows:

n is in A if all prime factors of n are greater than or equal to p_k,
n is in B if all prime factors of n are less than p_k; 1 is in B,
all other n are in C.

Each of the series $\sum\limits_{n \text{ in } A} \frac{1}{n}$, $\sum\limits_{n \text{ in } B} \frac{1}{n}$, and $\sum\limits_{n \text{ in } C} \frac{1}{n}$ converges, for since $\sum\limits_k^\infty \frac{1}{p_r}$ converges,

$$\sum_{n \text{ in } A} \frac{1}{n} < \sum_k^\infty \frac{1}{p_r} + \cdots + \left(\sum_k^\infty \frac{1}{p_r} \right)^s + \cdots = \frac{q}{1-q},$$

$$\sum_{n \text{ in } B} \frac{1}{n} = \frac{1}{1 - 1/p_1} \cdot \frac{1}{1 - 1/p_2} \cdots \frac{1}{1 - 1/p_{k-1}},$$

and

$$\sum_{n \text{ in } C} \frac{1}{n} < \left(\sum_{n \text{ in } A} \frac{1}{n} \right) \left(\sum_{n \text{ in } B} \frac{1}{n} \right).$$

Now,

$$\sum_1^n \frac{1}{n} = \sum_{n \text{ in } A} \frac{1}{n} + \sum_{n \text{ in } B} \frac{1}{n} + \sum_{n \text{ in } C} \frac{1}{n}$$

so that if $\sum_1^\infty \frac{1}{p_r}$ converges, so does $\sum_1^\infty \frac{1}{n}$. But $\sum_1^\infty \frac{1}{n}$ diverges.

42. If $0 < x < \pi/2$, then $-\frac{1}{2} \tan x/4 \leq \sum_1^n \sin kx \leq \frac{1}{2} \cot x/4$ $(n = 1, 2, \cdots)$.

43. If a, b, and c are the lengths of the sides of a triangle and if A is its area, then $a^2 + b^2 + c^2 > 4A\sqrt{3}$ unless $a = b = c$.

44. (I. Newton). Suppose $\prod_1^n a_i \neq 0$. Define $n + 1$ numbers p_i by

$$\prod_1^n (x + a_i) = \sum_0^n \binom{n}{k} p_k x^{n-k}.$$

(a) $p_{k-1}p_{k+1} < p_k^2$ $(k = 1, \cdots, n-1)$ unless $a_1 = a_2 = \cdots = a_n$. HINT: Consider $f(x,y) \equiv \sum_0^n \binom{n}{k} p_k x^{n-k} y^k$. Writing $f(x,y) = 0$ as an equation in x/y, one sees that all its roots are real. $f(0,y) \neq 0$. Consequently,

$$\frac{\partial^k}{\partial x^i \partial y^{k-1}} f(x,y) = 0,$$

considered as an equation in x, does not have 0 for a multiple root $(y \neq 0)$. Therefore, by Rolle's Theorem, $p_{k-1}t^2 + 2p_k t + p_{k+1} = 0$ has real roots not both zero. (Differentiate $f(x,y)$ with respect to x or y and apply Rolle's Theorem each time. In the end set $x/y = t$.)

(b) $p_k^{1/k} > p_{k+1}^{1/(k+1)}$ $(k = 1, \cdots, n-1)$ unless $a_1 = a_2 = \cdots = a_n$.

45. (a) If $0 < x < \pi/2$, then $\ln(\sec x) < \frac{1}{2} \sin x \tan x$.

(b) There are numbers a_p and b_p such that if $|x| \leq \pi/2$ and $p > 0$, then $|\sin x|^p \leq a_p \cos^p x + b_p \cos px$ $(p \neq 1, 3, 5, 7, \cdots)$.

46. Definition. If

$$f\left(\frac{x+y}{2}\right) \leq \frac{f(x) + f(y)}{2}$$

on an interval $[a,b]$, then f is *convex* on that interval.

(a) If f is convex on $[a,b]$,

$$f\left(\frac{\sum_1^n x_i}{n}\right) \leq \frac{\sum_1^n f(x_i)}{n}$$

on $[a,b]$. HINT: Adapt Cauchy's proof of the Theorem of Arithmetic and Geometric Means.

(b) What is the geometric interpretation of the above definition?

(c) Give several examples of functions convex on $[0,1]$.

(d) If f is twice differentiable on (a,b), then

$$f''(x) \geq 0 \quad \text{on} \quad (a,b)$$

is both a necessary and sufficient condition that f be convex on (a,b).

(e) If f is twice differentiable on (a,b), then

$$\begin{vmatrix} 1 & x_1 & f(x_1) \\ 1 & x_2 & f(x_2) \\ 1 & x_3 & f(x_3) \end{vmatrix} \geq 0 \quad (a < x_1 < x_2 < x_3 < b)$$

is equivalent to the condition that $f''(x) \geq 0$ on (a,b).

47. (a) A monotone increasing function of a convex function is convex.

(b) $\ln\left(\int_a^b |f(t)|^p \, dt\right)$ is a convex function of p for $p > 0$.

48. $\dfrac{1}{n} \sum_1^n \sin x_i \leq \sin\left(\dfrac{1}{n} \sum_1^n x_i\right)$ if $0 < x_1 < \cdots < x_n < \pi$.

49. If $x > y > 0$ and $r > 1$, then

$$ry^{r-1} < \frac{x^r - y^r}{x - y} < rx^{r-1};$$

if $0 < r < 1$, then

$$rx^{r-1} < \frac{x^r - y^r}{x - y} < ry^{r-1}.$$

HINT: If $a > 1$, $ra^r > \sum_0^{n-1} a^k$; hence,

$$\frac{a^{r+1} - 1}{r + 1} > \frac{a^r - 1}{r}.$$

Also, if $0 < b < 1$,

$$\frac{1 - b^{r+1}}{r + 1} < \frac{1 - b^r}{r}.$$

Thus if $r > s$,

$$\frac{a^r - 1}{r} > \frac{a^s - 1}{s} \quad \text{and} \quad \frac{1 - b^r}{r} < \frac{1 - b^s}{s}.$$

50. If $v_1 \geq v_2 \geq \cdots \geq v_n \geq 0$, then

$$\left| \sum_1^n u_i v_i \right| \leq v_1 \max_{1 \leq k \leq n} \left| \sum_1^k u_i \right|$$

HINT: $\sum_1^n u_i v_i \equiv \sum_{k=1}^{n-1} \left(\sum_1^k u_i \right) (v_k - v_{k+1}) + v_n \sum_1^n u_k.$

51. If f is positive and monotone increasing for $x \geq 0$, and if $F(x) = \int_0^x f(t)\, dt$ and $F_n = \sum_0^n f(k)$, then

$$F(n) \leq F_n \leq F(n) + f(n).$$

52. (Jensen's Inequality). If $p_i > 0$ $(i = 1, \cdots, n)$ and if f is convex on (a,b), then

$$f\left(\frac{\sum_1^n p_i x_i}{\sum_1^n p_i} \right) \leq \frac{\sum_1^n p_i f(x_i)}{\sum_1^n p_i} \quad \text{on } (a,b).$$

53. (W. H. Young). If $f(0) = 0$ and f is strictly increasing for $x \geq 0$ and if g is the inverse function to f, then for a and b positive

$$ab \leq \int_0^a f(x)\, dx + \int_0^b g(y)\, dy.$$

Equality holds if and only if $b = f(a)$.
HINT: Sketch the graphs of f and g plotting $f(x)$ against x and $g(y)$ against y. Use just one set of coordinate axes.

54. If one suitably chooses f and g, then by W. H. Young's Theorem, it follows that if a and b are positive,

$$ab \leq \frac{a^p}{p} + \frac{b^q}{q}, \quad \text{where} \quad \frac{1}{p} + \frac{1}{q} = 1 \quad (p > 1).$$

55. (a) If f is continuous on $[a,b]$, then

$$\lim_{p \to \infty} \left[\int_a^b |f(x)|^p \, dx \right]^{1/p} = \text{l.u.b.}_{a \le x \le b} |f(x)| \equiv M.$$

HINT: On one hand, choose any m such that $0 < m < M$, and integrate over the set of points where $|f(x)| \ge m$. Then let m increase to M.

(b) Let f be continuous in the rectangle where $a \le x \le b$ and $c \le y \le d$, and let

$$F(x) = \int_c^d f(x,y) \, dy,$$

then $\left(\int_a^b |F(x)|^p \, dx \right)^{1/p} \le \int_c^d \left[\int_a^b |f(x,y)|^p \, dx \right]^{1/p} dy \quad (p \ge 1).$

56. If f is convex on (a,b), then the limit $\lim_{h \to 0^+} \dfrac{f(x+h) - f(x)}{h}$ exists for x on (a,b). This limit is, of course, called the right-hand derivative of f at x. Show also that this derivative is monotone on (a,b).

57. If f is convex on $[a,b]$, if $a \le g(x) \le b$ for $c \le x \le d$, and if the integrals below exist, then

$$f\left[\int_c^d g(x) \, dx \right] \le \int_c^d f[g(x)] \, dx.$$

58. If $0 < x < \pi$, then $\displaystyle\sum_1^n \frac{\sin kx}{k} > 0 \quad (n = 1, 2, \cdots).$

HINT: Use induction. Suppose $s_k(x) \equiv \displaystyle\sum_1^k (\sin lx)/l > 0 \quad (k = 1, \cdots, n-1).$ Further suppose $s_n(x_0) \le 0$ for some x_0 on $(0,\pi)$ and that $s_n(x_0)$ is a minimum for $s_n(x)$. Use the facts below.

$$s_n'(x_0) = \frac{\sin (n + \tfrac{1}{2})x_0 - \sin \tfrac{1}{2}x_0}{2 \sin \tfrac{1}{2}x_0} = 0 \quad \text{(Why? Sum } \sum_1^n \sin kx.\text{)}$$

$$\sin nx_0 = \sin (n + \tfrac{1}{2})x_0 \cos \tfrac{1}{2}x_0 - \cos (n + \tfrac{1}{2})x_0 \sin \tfrac{1}{2}x_0.$$

59. If f is nonnegative and continuous on $(0,\pi)$, then

$$\left| \int_0^\pi f(x) \sin nx \, dx \right| < \int_0^\pi f(x) \sin x \, dx \quad \text{unless} \quad f \equiv 0.$$

60. The function P whose values $P(r,t)$ are given by $P(r,t) = \dfrac{1}{2} \dfrac{1 - r}{1 - 2r \cos t + t^2}$ is called the Poisson kernel.

(a) If $0 \le r \le 1$, then

$$P(r,t) = \frac{1}{2} + \sum_0^\infty r^k \cos kt = \mathcal{R}\left(\frac{1}{2} + \sum_1^\infty z^k \right) = \mathcal{R}\left(\frac{1}{2} \cdot \frac{1 - z}{1 + z} \right),$$

where $z = re^{it}$.

(b) If $0 \le r < 1$, then

$$\frac{1}{2} \cdot \frac{1 - r}{1 + r} \le P(r,t) \le \frac{1}{2} \cdot \frac{1 + r}{1 - r}.$$

(c) If $\frac{1}{2} \leq r < 1$,

$$P(r,t) < \frac{\pi^2}{2} \cdot \frac{1-r}{(1-r)^2 + t^2}.$$

(d) If $0 < x < \pi$,

$$\int_0^{\pi - x} (t+x)P(r,t)\, dt - \int_x^\pi tP(r,t)\, dt < \frac{3\pi x}{2}.$$

HINT: $\dfrac{1}{\pi} \displaystyle\int_{-\pi}^\pi P(r,t)\, dt = 1.$

61. If y is defined and real on $(0,\pi)$, if $y(0) = y(\pi) = 0$, if y' is in $L_2(0,\pi)$ and if $y(x) = \int_0^x y'(t)\, dt$, then

$$\int_0^\pi y^2(x)\, dx < \int_0^\pi y'^2(x)\, dx$$

unless y is a multiple of $\sin x$. HINT: Show that $\lim_{x \to 0^+} x^{-1/2}y(x) = 0$ and that

$$\int_0^\pi (y'^2 - y^2)\, dx = \int_0^\pi (y' - y \cot x)^2\, dx.$$

62. (E. Landau). If f is twice continuously differentiable on $[0, \infty)$, and if f'' and f are bounded for $x \geq 0$, then

$$\max_{x \geq 0} |f'(x)| \leq 4 (\max_{x \geq 0} |f|) (\max_{x \geq 0} |f''|).$$

Some of the following geometrical theorems are really still conjectures since they have never been proved. Several of the rest are also challenging. You can find helpful discussions of extremal problems in geometry in the following works: *Maxima und Minima in der Elementaren Geometrie* by R. Sturm (B. G. Teubner, Berlin, 1910), *Convex Figures* by I. M. Yaglom and V. G. Boltyanskiĭ (translation by Paul J. Kelly and Lewis F. Walton, Holt, Rinehart and Winston, 1961), and *Geometric Inequalities* by N. D. Kazarinoff (Wesleyan Univ. Press and Random House, 1961).

63. Of all triangles inscribed in a given triangle (one vertex on each side), the one formed by the feet of the altitudes of the given triangle has the least perimeter.

64. Definition. The *diameter* of a set is the least upper bound of the distances between pairs of points of the set.
    If A is the area of an n-gon of diameter 1, then

$$A \leq \frac{n}{2} \cos\left(\frac{\pi}{n}\right) \tan\left(\frac{\pi}{2n}\right).$$

65. If one inscribes a triangle in a given triangle, the given triangle is subdivided into four smaller ones.
  (a) Of these, the inscribed triangle never has strictly the least area. HINT: Find out what an affine transformation is.
  (b) (Conjecture). Of these, the inscribed triangle never has strictly the least perimeter.

66. Of all quadrilateral prisms with a given volume, the cube has the least surface area.

67. Let ABC be a triangle, and let P be a point in its interior. Let $R_A = \overline{PA}$, $R_B = \overline{PB}$, and $R_C = \overline{PC}$. Denote the distance from P to AB by p_C, to BC by p_A, and to CA by p_B.

(a) $\dfrac{R_A}{R_A + p_A} + \dfrac{R_B}{R_B + p_B} + \dfrac{R_C}{R_C + p_C} \geq 2.$

(b) $R_A R_B R_C \geq 8 p_A p_B p_C.$

(c) (P. Erdös). $R_A + R_B + R_C \geq 2(p_A + p_B + p_C).$
When does equality hold?

68. (D. K. Kazarinoff). If $ABCD$ is a tetrahedron, P is a point within it, $R_A = \overline{PA}$, p_A is the distance from P to the face BCD, etc., then

$$R_A + R_B + R_C + R_D > 2\sqrt{2}\,(p_A + p_B + p_C + p_D).$$

Proofs of this theorem are known only in case $ABCD$ is a trirectangular tetrahedron or in case the circumcenter of $ABCD$ does not lie outside of $ABCD$.

69. (P. Ungar). Let n points be given in the plane, not all on a straight line, then the shortest closed route connecting them is a simple polygon.

70. (Conjecture made by P. Ungar). Given a plane convex body B with two perpendicular chords that cut its perimeter into four equal parts, then twice the sum of the lengths of the chords is at least the perimeter of B. Equality holds only for rectangles.

(a) Prove the conjecture when the chords also bisect each other.
(b) Prove the conjecture when the chords bisect each other but are not necessarily perpendicular.
(c) Try other special cases—even the general one.

71. *Conjecture:* Under the assumptions of Ungar's conjecture, the sum of the lengths of the chords is at least the diameter of B.

Index